American Language Hub

STARTER A
Workbook

with Key + access to Audio

macmillan education

Macmillan Education
4 Crinan Street
London N1 9XW
A division of Macmillan Education Limited

Companies and representatives throughout the world

American Language Hub Starter A Workbook with Key
ISBN 978-1-380-04679-6
American Language Hub Starter A Workbook with Key + access to
Audio ISBN 978-1-380-04673-4

Written by Signature Manuscripts

First published 2020

Original design by emc design ltd
Page make-up by SPi Global
Illustrated by Nigel Dobbyn (Beehive Illustration) pp14, 16, 21
Cover design based on original design by Restless
Cover photograph by Getty Images/Valentinrussanov
Picture research by Emily Taylor

The author and publishers would like to thank the following for permission to reproduce their photographs:
Alamy/AY Images p10(brazil), Alamy/Rimma Bondarenko p32(l), Alamy/MYALA88 p10(china), Alamy/Neftali p10(egypt), Alamy/Shattha Pilabut p17(tl), Alamy/Tetra Images p8(bl); **Getty Images**/10'000 Hours p21(mr), Getty Images/Andresr pp26(a), 38(tr), Getty Images/Thomas Barwick pp26(inset), Getty Images/Caiaimage/Martin Barraud p4, Getty Images/Doug Berry p14(tr), Getty Images/Katarzyna Bialasiewicz p36(b), Getty Images/EyeEm/Alan Brutenic p25, Getty Images/Caiaimage/Sam Edwards p8(tr), Getty Images/Neale Clark p38(cm), Getty Images/John Coletti p11(bl), Getty Images/Dean Conger p26(tl), Getty Images/Cultura/Philipp Nemenz p15(tr), Getty Images/Nick David p39, Getty Images/Peter Dazeley p27(tl), Getty Images/Dulin p20(tr), Getty Images/EyeEm/Daniel Limpi p14(mr), Getty Images/EyeEm/Arisara Tongdonnoi p12, Getty Images/Lívia Fernandes p9(tl), Getty Images/Johnny Greig p15(tl), Getty Images/GuruXOOX p33(tl), Getty Images/Hero Images pp6(br), 22, Getty Images/Hinterhaus Productions p26(b), Getty Images/Gary Houlder p6(bl), Getty Images/Image Source p24(tr), Getty Images/Imaginima p36(tr), Getty Images/iStockphoto pp11(tl), 21(bl), 37, Getty Images/Kool99 p10(mali), Getty Images/Matelly p21(br), Getty Images/Michelle McMahon p10(br), Getty Images/Jasmin Merdan p31, Getty Images/Mint Images p35, Getty Images/Monkeybusinessimages p18(b), Getty Images/Morsa Images pp18(tl), 21(tl), Getty Images/Peter Muller p13, Getty Images/Nd3000 p33(br), Getty Images/Ian Nolan p17(br), Getty Images/Getty Images/PeopleImages p27(bl), Getty Images/PhotoDisc p38(cl), Getty Images/Andrey Popov p30, Getty Images/Raclro p10(poland, sweden), Getty Images/Tim Robberts pp9(bl) Getty Images/RoBeDeRo p34, Getty Images/Oliver Rossi p5, Getty Images/Smith Collection p23, Getty Images/SolStock p32(r), Getty Images/Sturti p28(b), Getty Images/Denis Tangney Jr p11(ml), Getty Images/Traveler1116 p10(japan), Getty Images/Tunart p10(turkey), Getty Images/Skynesher p14(br), Getty Images/Vasilis Tsikkinis photos p24(b), Getty Images/Corin Walker Bain p36(tm), Getty Images/Tom Werner p7, Getty Images/Westend61 pp11(backround), 28(inset), Getty Images/Pawel Wewiorski p20(bl), Getty Images/Zstockphotos p36(tl); **PeopleImages** p14(bl); **SolStock** p29.

Printed and bound in Mexico
by Compañía Editorial Ultra, S.A. de C.V.

2021 2020
04 03 02 01

Contents

1.1 Nice to meet you!

Say hello

VOCABULARY
Countries

Complete the short conversations with the names of the countries.

A: Hi! Nice to meet you! I'm Wanda. I'm from [1]C ___ na ___ ___.

B: Nice to meet you too, Wanda. I'm Danny. I'm from [2]B ___ ___ z ___ ___.

A: Are you from [3]A ___ g ___ ___ ___ ___ n ___?

B: No, I'm from [4]M ___ x ___ ___ ___.

A: Hello. I'm Jack. I'm from [5]B ___ ___ t ___ in.

B: Nice to meet you, Jack. I'm Ali and I'm from [6]Mo ___ ___ c ___ ___.

A: This is Mount Fuji. Where is it?

B: It's in [7]J ___ ___ a ___.

A: Where's the Leaning Tower of Pisa?

B: It's in [8]I ___ ___ ___ y.

A: The Pyramids are in [9]E ___ ___ p ___.

B: Yes, and Sydney Opera House is in [10]Au ___ ___ r ___ ___ i ___.

A: I'm from [11]S ___ ___ i ___. Are you from [12]T ___ ___ k ___ ___?

B: Yes, that's right.

Numbers 0–10

A Write the numbers out in words.

- **a** 1 ___*one*___
- **b** 9 ______
- **c** 3 ______
- **d** 6 ______
- **e** 2 ______
- **f** 10 ______
- **g** 8 ______
- **h** 4 ______
- **i** 7 ______
- **j** 5 ______

B Match the phone numbers in words (1–6) with the phone numbers in figures (a–f).

1. five, one, six, four, one, seven, three, two, nine, two ___
2. four, one, eight, seven, nine, eight, two, three, eight, seven ___
3. five, six, four, seven, one, three, two, nine, five, three ___
4. four, one, eight, seven, eight, nine, two, one, one, two ___
5. five, six, four, seven, one, nine, three, two, five, three ___
6. four, one, eight, seven, one, eight, nine, two, one, zero ___

- **a** 564-713-2953
- **b** 564-719-3253
- **c** 418-718-9210
- **d** 418-798-2387
- **e** 418-789-2112
- **f** 516-417-3292

1.1 Nice to meet you!

PRONUNCIATION
Syllables and syllable stress

A Which syllable is stressed? Write the words in the table.

Argentina Australia China Egypt Italy Japan Mexico Morocco Spain Turkey

●	●⬤	⬤●	⬤●●	●⬤●	●⬤●●	●●⬤●
1 ______	Brazil	3 ______	Canada	8 ______	9 ______	10 ______
	2 ______	4 ______	6 ______			
		5 ______	7 ______			

.1 **B** Listen and check your answers to Exercise A.

.2 **C** Practice saying the cities and countries. Then listen and check.

1 Berlin, Germany
2 Budapest, Hungary
3 Bogotá, Colombia
4 Jakarta, Indonesia
5 Moscow, Russia
6 Stockholm, Sweden

D Add the countries from Exercise C to the table in Exercise A.

GRAMMAR
Simple present *be*: *I*, *you*

A Choose the correct options to complete the sentences.

1 You ___ from Morocco.
   a is   b are
2 ___ from Germany. I'm from Austria.
   a I don't   b I'm not
3 ___ from Indonesia, right?
   a You are   b You is
4 So, ___ from Britain. Where are you from?
   a you not   b you're not
5 **A:** ___ from Australia?
   B: No, I'm from New Zealand.
   a You are   b Are you
6 Hi. ___ Salvatore from Italy.
   a I am   b I'm am

B Complete the missing information.

1 **Positive:** I am / I'm from Spain.
   Negative: ______________.
   Question: Am I from Spain?
   Short answer: Yes, I am. / ______________.
2 **Positive:** ______________.
   Negative: You are not happy. / You aren't happy. / You're not happy.
   Question: ______________?
   Short answer: Yes, I am. / No, I'm not.
3 **Positive:** I am from Egypt. / I'm from Egypt.
   Negative: I am not from Egypt. / I'm not from Egypt.
   Question: ______________?
   Short answer: ______________ / No, I'm not.

C Complete the conversation with the correct form of the verb *be*.

A: Hi, [1] ______________ Maria. [2] ______________ from Mexico.
B: Nice to meet you, Maria. [3] ______________ David.
A: Nice to meet you, David. [4] ______________ from Britain?
B: No, [5] ______________. [6] ______________ from Melbourne in Australia.

VOCABULARY
Jobs

A Look at the puzzle and find 18 words for jobs.

q	c	o	m	p	u	t	e	r	p	r	o	g	r	a	m	m	e	r	r
d	o	c	t	o	r	t	y	s	o	c	c	e	r	p	l	a	y	e	r
e	n	g	i	n	e	e	r	o	s	h	k	l	p	m	s	b	r	p	e
x	n	t	p	m	m	q	k	o	c	a	s	u	v	u	s	p	a	d	c
t	m	b	u	i	l	d	e	r	h	r	t	c	b	s	f	h	m	l	e
e	f	v	a	n	r	q	r	g	e	d	u	a	t	i	z	o	a	p	p
a	s	d	r	n	r	z	r	h	f	y	d	w	s	c	v	t	n	y	t
c	j	d	e	s	i	g	n	e	r	d	e	r	u	i	u	o	a	q	i
h	o	y	c	t	o	g	s	c	b	e	n	r	o	a	i	g	g	u	o
e	p	t	c	p	h	p	k	z	a	m	t	e	a	n	l	r	e	r	n
r	a	r	w	r	i	t	e	r	a	u	j	a	c	k	l	a	r	d	i
h	c	q	f	i	t	l	k	r	l	s	c	p	c	t	r	p	h	b	s
l	t	n	s	a	l	e	s	c	l	e	r	k	a	n	t	h	k	n	t
p	o	l	i	c	e	o	f	f	i	c	e	r	c	e	a	e	v	n	m
a	r	c	h	i	t	e	c	t	r	r	o	c	t	w	w	r	u	v	e

1 ______
2 ______
3 ______
4 ______
5 ______
6 ______
7 ______
8 ______
9 ______
10 ______
11 ______
12 ______
13 ______
14 ______
15 ______
16 ______
17 ______
18 ______

B Choose the correct options to complete the texts.

About | Profile | Blog | Contact

I'm [1]***a designer* / *a doctor*** in a company. It's a small team and I'm busy. My colleagues are very nice. My [2]***musician* / *manager***, Helen, is OK. Annette is the [3]***receptionist* / *police officer***. She answers the phone.

About | Profile | Blog | Contact

I'm Jonas and I'm [4]***a teacher* / *an engineer***. My job is at a big language school. My [5]***students* / *engineers*** are from Brazil and Mexico. I'm also a [6]***computer programmer* / *writer***. I write English books for my school.

GRAMMAR

Simple present *be*: *he, she, it*

A **Complete the sentences with the words and phrases in the box.**

he's is Is it isn't it is It's not She's

1 Jake ________________ an architect. His job is great.
2 Sylvia ________________ a teacher – she's a student!
3 I love my job. ________________ fun.
4 Fred isn't a designer; ________________ a photographer.
5 **A:** Is your job OK?
B: Yes, ________________.
6 This is Yasmin. ________________ a police officer.
7 You're from Denmark? Wow! ________________ nice there?
8 My manager is here. She's ________________ very busy today.

B **Complete the questions and answers with one or two words in each blank.**

1 Is Peter a teacher?
No, ________________. He's a doctor.
2 ________________ a small team?
Yes, it is.
3 Is she busy today?
Yes, ________________. She's very busy.
4 Is David your colleague?
No, he isn't. ________________ my manager.
5 Is it a big company?
Yes, it is. ________________ very big!
6 ________________ nice?
No, she isn't nice and she isn't friendly.

PRONUNCIATION

Contractions with *be*

A **Practice saying the sentences aloud. Be careful with the underlined phrases.**

1 He's from Brazil.
2 It's great here!
3 Gemma? She's very nice.
4 It isn't my first day.
5 She's from Australia. She's new here, too.
6 He isn't my colleague. He's my friend.

1.3 **B** **Listen and check (✓) the sentence you hear. Practice saying the sentences in the same way as the speakers in the recording.**

1 a She isn't nice. ☐
b She's really nice. ☐
2 a It isn't fun! ☐
b It's fun! ☐
3 a She's my manager. ☐
b She isn't my manager. ☐
4 a He's from Egypt. ☐
b He isn't from Egypt. ☐
5 a He's a doctor. ☐
b She's a doctor. ☐
6 a He's new today. ☐
b She's new today. ☐
7 a She's busy today. ☐
b She isn't busy today. ☐
8 a It's a big team. ☐
b It isn't a big team. ☐

READING

A READ FOR GIST Read the email. Where is Kitty's job?

Re: My new job
To: MatteoRossi@facespace.net
From: kittyd@smail.net

Hi Matteo,

How are you? I'm happy because today is the first day at my new job. [1]**It**'s fun. I'm a receptionist at a language school in New York City. [2]**It**'s big and there are hundreds of students. They come from Turkey, Spain, Egypt, Japan and other countries. This is a picture of me at work.

Today is the first day for the students, too. I write the names, addresses and phone numbers on the registration form. My colleague isn't here today, so I'm very busy. [3]**She**'s from Australia and her name is Anna.

Now I'm in the café. [4]**It**'s small, but it's nice. My manager, David, is with me. [5]**He**'s friendly.

How's *your* new job? And where is [6]**it**? Is it in Boston? Please tell me all about it!

See you soon!

Kitty

B READ FOR DETAIL Read the email again and answer the questions.

1. What is Kitty's job?
2. Is the school big or small?
3. What information is on the registration form?
4. Where is Kitty's colleague from?
5. Where is Kitty now?
6. Is her manager friendly?

C IDENTIFY PERSONAL PRONOUNS What do the words in **bold** in the email refer to?

1. *the new job*
2. ______
3. ______
4. ______
5. ______
6. ______

D REFLECT Think about the answers to these questions.

1. What is your job?
2. Are you happy with your job?

LISTENING

A PREDICT Look at the picture. Do you think the people know each other?

1.4 **B LISTEN FOR GIST** Listen to a conversation. Where are the people?

1.4 **C LISTEN FOR DETAIL** Listen again and complete the information about the people.

Woman

First name:	[1] ______
Job:	[2] ______

Man

First name:	[3] ______
Last name:	*Abboud*
Job:	[4] ______ *on a design course*
Home (city, country):	*Alexandria,* [5] ______
Classroom number:	[6] ______
Time:	[7] ______

D REFLECT Think about the answers to these questions.

1. Which country do you think is good for an English language school: Britain, Australia, the US or a different country?
2. Are the students in your English class all from your country, or are they from different countries?

FUNCTIONAL LANGUAGE
Greeting people

A Complete the conversation between Laura and Callum with the words and phrases (a–j).

a No, I'm not
b later
c Hi
d Are you from New York
e see you
f Bye
g Yes, I am
h Where are you from
i Nice to meet you
j last

Callum: [1] ________! My name's Callum. I'm from Canada.
Laura: Hello, Callum. [2] ________. I'm Laura. I'm from America.
Callum: [3] ________?
Laura: [4] ________. I'm from Boston.
Callum: Are you a student?
Laura: No, I'm a computer programmer. Are you a student?
Callum: [5] ________.
Laura: [6] ________ in Canada?
Callum: Vancouver.
Laura: What's your [7] ________ name, Callum?
Callum: Westbrook. I'm Callum Westbrook. And you?
Laura: Price. Laura Price.
Callum: Well, um, nice to meet you, Laura. See you [8] ________.
Laura: Yes, [9] ________ in class.
Callum: OK, then. [10] ________.
Laura: Bye.

B Now listen to the conversation and check your answers to Exercise A.

WRITING

A Which words in the box need capital letters? Why?

austria berlin carlbeck@zmail.net engineer fashion designer helena jones simon stockholm

B **USING CAPITAL LETTERS** Find and correct the mistakes with capital letters in the form.

Purcell Recreational Center
Registration Form

First name:	alexander
Last name:	sparks
Home (city, country):	glasgow, scotland
Job:	architect
Telephone number:	01414 960599
Email:	alexsparks@amail.net

WRITING PRACTICE

WRITE Complete the form with information about a friend. Do not forget to use capital letters for names and places.

Purcell Recreational Center
Registration Form

First name:	________
Last name:	________
Home (city, country):	________
Job:	________
Telephone number:	________
Email:	________

VOCABULARY
Languages and nationalities

A Complete the nationalities.

Country: Brazil
Nationality: [1] ________________

Country: China
Nationality: [2] ________________

Country: Egypt
Nationality: [3] ________________

Country: Japan
Nationality: [4] ________________

Country: Mali
Nationality: [5] ________________

Country: Poland
Nationality: [6] ________________

Country: Sweden
Nationality: [7] ________________

Country: Turkey
Nationality: [8] ________________

B Complete the sentences with the correct languages and nationalities.

1 I'm Mohammed. I'm ________________. I'm from Algeria.
2 No, we aren't ________________. We aren't from Lebanon.
3 Our teacher is ________________. He's from Venezuela.
4 Rome is in Italy. They speak ________________ there.
5 **A:** Is Khanh from Vietnam?
B: Yes, she is. She's ________________.
6 The Proclaimers are a band from Scotland. They're ________________.
7 **A:** What language is that?
B: It's ________________. Those people are from Portugal.
8 I'm in Denmark, but I don't understand the people here. ________________ is a difficult language.

PRONUNCIATION
Syllable stress

A Read the sentences. Underline the stressed syllables in the countries and nationalities.

1 We're from Poland. We're Polish.
2 He's Canadian – you know, from Canada.
3 She's from Turkey. She's Turkish.
4 You're Swedish … from Sweden, right?
5 It's from Egypt. It's Egyptian.
6 The singer is from China. He's Chinese.
7 Alva is an Icelandic name. I'm from Iceland.
8 The songs are from Italy. They're in Italian.

2.1 **B** Listen and check your answers to Exercise A. Then listen again and repeat.

2.1 Our music, our world

Where are they from? ______

GRAMMAR

Simple present *be*: *we, you, they*

Complete the text with the words in the box.

are · Are you · aren't · They're · We're · you

1 ______ ready for some great American music?
This week: three ideas for your playlist from the US …

Sean Rowe is a musician and songwriter from Troy, New York. His music is very cool. 2 ______ big fans!

St. Vincent (real name, Annie Clark) is a singer and songwriter from Oklahoma. Are 3 ______ a fan of her music? We 4 ______. Her songs 5 ______ boring – they're very interesting. We love her album *Masseduction*.

The Revivalists is a band of eight people from New Orleans. 6 ______ super cool!

Possessive adjectives

A Complete the table with the correct possessive adjectives or subject pronouns.

Subject pronouns	Possessive adjectives
I love pop music.	1 ______ favorite pop star is Ariana Grande.
2 ______ are a great singer.	Your songs are beautiful.
He is from Virginia.	3 ______ name is James.
This song isn't very good.	4 ______ name is 'La la la'.
5 ______ is a jazz musician.	Her music is very modern.
We have a new album.	6 ______ fans are very excited!
7 ______ have two guitarists in their band.	Their names are Sara and Thomas.

B Complete the sentences with a possessive adjective in each blank.

1. Tommy is ______ friend. The two of us are in a band.
2. This is The Revivalists's album. ______ name is *Take Good Care*.
3. You're a good songwriter. ______ songs are great.
4. We love it. It's on ______ playlist.
5. She's a good singer, but ______ songs are very sad!
6. I love this band. ______ music is great!
7. He is a great singer. ______ music is really good.

2.2 Our music, our world

When are you free?

VOCABULARY
Days of the week

A Reorder the letters to make days of the week.

1 Wydaednse ______
2 Tduyesa ______
3 Syudtara ______
4 Maonyd ______
5 Tsuyradh ______
6 Fyiadr ______
7 Sayund ______

B Put the days of the week in Exercise A in the correct order.

1 *Monday*
2 ______
3 ______
4 ______
5 ______
6 ______
7 ______

Numbers 11–100

A Write the numbers in words. Underline the stressed syllables.

1 11 ______
2 20 ______
3 90 ______
4 12 ______
5 19 ______
6 36 ______
7 50 ______
8 15 ______

B Match the words (1–8) to the numbers (a–h).

1 forty-four	a 31
2 seventeen	b 44
3 fifty-three	c 53
4 nineteen	d 64
5 ninety-eight	e 17
6 thirty-one	f 98
7 eighty-seven	g 87
8 sixty-four	h 19

C Write the numbers in digits.

1 eleven ______
2 fourteen ______
3 forty-four ______
4 fifty-two ______
5 sixty-seven ______
6 ninety-nine ______

GRAMMAR
Wh- questions with *be*

A Complete the conversation with one to three words in each blank.

A: Hello!
B: Good morning.
A: What's [1] _______________?
B: It's Lucas Charpentier.
A: Where [2] _______________ from?
B: Nantes, in France.
A: And how [3] _______________?
B: I'm 32.
A: [4] _______________ in this photo?
B: My children.
A: What [5] _______________?
B: Stephan and Naomi.
A: [6] _______________ your English classes?
B: On Tuesdays and Thursdays.
A: OK! Thank you. Bye.
B: See you soon.

B Find and correct the mistakes in the questions. Do not use short forms (~~*What's, Where's, Who's*~~, etc).

1 Where John is from? I don't think he is from the US.
____

2 I'm Ellen. What's is your name?
____

3 Jane's nice. Where are she from?
____

4 Who's is your teacher? I have Mr. Smith.
____

5 How old your children are?
____

6 I love Anna Calvi. What is your favorite singer?
____

7 From where is your English teacher?
____

8 This class looks fun. How old the teacher is?
____

PRONUNCIATION
Contractions in questions

A Practice saying the questions aloud.

1 a How's your yoga class? ☐
b Where's your yoga class? ☐
2 a Where's your house? ☐
b How old's your house? ☐
3 a Who are you? ☐
b How are you? ☐
4 a Where's this? ☐
b Who's this? ☐
5 a Who's your teacher? ☐
b How's your teacher? ☐
6 a Who are they? ☐
b How are they? ☐

2.2 **B** Read the questions in Exercise A again. Listen and check (✓) the question you hear.

READING

A SCAN FOR INFORMATION Look at the poster and the picture. Where is the music festival?

The Shamrock Music Festival

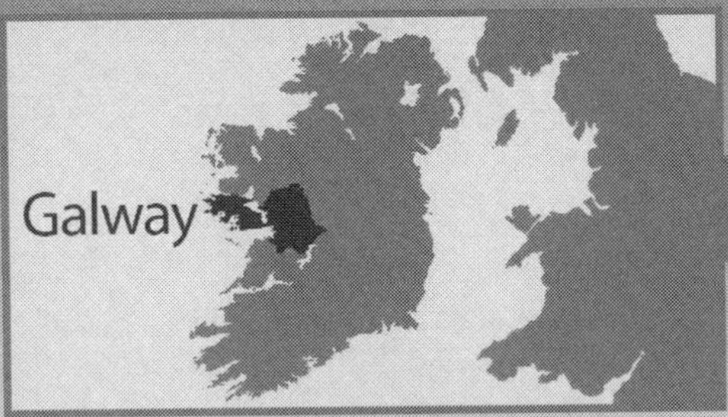

What is it?

It's a festival of Irish music from Ireland and other countries – Canada, Britain and Australia, too!

Where is it?

It's in Galway in Ireland. It's very nice there and the people are friendly. They're really fun, too!

When is it?

It's on Friday, Saturday and Sunday.

What are the bands?

The big star of the festival is Druve. She's an Irish singer and songwriter from Dublin. Her songs are from her album *Fly on Hill*. Blast Faster is a Canadian musician. His songs are in English and they're great! And 30 more bands!

B READ FOR DETAIL Read the poster and answer the questions.

1 Where are the musicians from?
2 What's the name of the festival town?
3 What days is the festival?
4 Who's the big star of the festival?
5 Where's she from?
6 How many other bands are there?

C REFLECT Think about the answers to these questions.

1 Is there a summer music festival in your country?
2 Do you like music festivals?

LISTENING

A PREPARE TO LISTEN Look at the flyer. Which music looks good?

The Music Box

Saturday [1] ____________ **am**
Workshop about music from [2] ____________

Saturday 7 pm
African Music Night! Music from [3] ____________, Morocco and Algeria

Sunday 9 am – 11 am
Children's singing workshop

[4] ____________ **8 pm**
[5] ____________ music from Turkey – Istanbul Sound System play songs from their new album.

2.3 **B LISTEN FOR GIST** Listen to a phone conversation and choose the correct options to complete the sentences.

1 The woman is a *musician / receptionist*.
2 The man's name is *Pedro / Richard*.
3 The man buys tickets for the *African Music Night / children's singing workshop*.

2.3 **C LISTEN FOR DETAIL** Listen again and complete the flyer with one word or number in each blank.

D REFLECT Think about the answers to these questions.

1 Which music from the flyer do you want to listen to?
2 Would you like to go to a singing workshop? Why/Why not?

FUNCTIONAL LANGUAGE
Asking for clarification

A Complete the conversation with the words in the box. There are two extra words.

fashion	from	how	job	mean	new
sorry	understand	What	Where		

Sean: Hi, everyone. Ben and Soraya are [1] ________ students.
Maria: Hi! Please sit down and have some coffee.
Aliki: Where are you [2] ________, Ben?
Ben: I'm from France. I'm French.
Maria: What's your [3] ________?
Ben: I'm a *créateur*.
Maria: A what? [4] ________ does that [5] ________?
Sean: Designer. And what do you design?
Ben: I design clothes.
Aliki: Oh. You're a [6] ________ designer!
Ben: Yes, that's it.
Sean: And what about you, Soraya?
Soraya: I'm from Iran. I'm a … I think the English word is 'boss'.
Maria: A manager?
Soraya: Yes, a manager.
Erik: I'm [7] ________, I don't [8] ________. What do you manage?
Soraya: It's my job. I'm the manager of a bank.

B Listen to the conversation and check your answers to Exercise A.

WRITING

Hancock's English School

Home Forum About Login Sign up

Hi, everybody!
My name's Freddy. I'm from Vienna in Austria. I'm 25 years old. I'm an engineer. <u>My English classes are on Mondays, Wednesdays and Fridays</u>. My teacher is Mrs. Jane Cloud. She's from Des Moines in Iowa. <u>I'm a big fan of jazz</u>. My favorite band is The Necks. They're from Australia.

A Read the online introduction and answer the questions.

1 Where is Freddy from?
____

2 How old is Freddy?
____

3 Who is Mrs. Jane Cloud?
____

4 Where is Mrs. Cloud from?
____

5 What's Freddy's favorite music?
____

B **USING *AND* TO JOIN SENTENCES** Read the introduction again. Add *and* four times to Freddy's introduction to join sentences together. Do not join the <u>underlined</u> sentences.

WRITING PRACTICE

WRITE Write an online introduction for your school message board. Use Freddy's introduction to help you. Do not forget to use *and* to join sentences.

VOCABULARY
Objects and colors

A Look at the puzzle and find eight words for colors.

s	m	b	r	o	s	l	u	e	t
w	y	e	l	l	o	w	e	d	b
b	l	u	w	n	g	r	e	e	r
l	l	o	w	a	c	k	e	r	o
a	c	k	r	e	d	g	o	e	w
c	g	r	e	u	o	r	e	y	n
k	p	i	n	t	r	a	b	b	c
w	h	i	l	t	e	y	s	k	v
w	g	r	e	e	n	t	x	a	h
h	c	l	l	o	d	s	a	l	m
i	b	r	o	u	d	e	t	c	h
t	r	e	a	d	g	h	t	a	n
e	d	s	a	y	b	l	u	e	i

1 ____________
2 ____________
3 ____________
4 ____________
5 ____________
6 ____________
7 ____________
8 ____________

B Look at the pictures and complete the short conversations with one word in each blank. The first letter is given to help you.

Mark: Nice [1]h______________!
Sarah: Thanks! It's new.
Mark: Your [2]c______________ is the same color.
Sarah: Yes, it is!

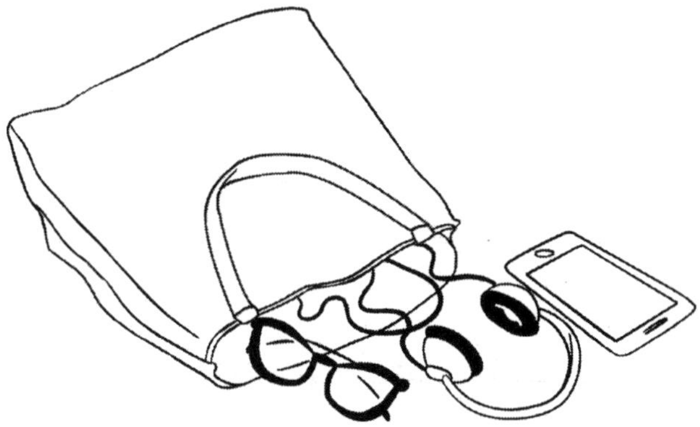

Antonio: This is nice.
Maria: Yes, it's my new [3]b______________.
Antonio: It isn't very big.
Maria: No, it isn't, but it's OK. It's for my [4]p______________, my [5]g______________ and my [6]h______________.

Ellie: Cool [7]s______________!
Dan: Thanks! Nice [8]u______________!
Ellie: Thank you!

Sara: Wow! I like your [9]______________.
Emily: Thanks! They're new.

GRAMMAR
a/an and plural nouns

Choose the correct options to complete the sentences.

1 This is ____ umbrella from China.
 a an
 b a
2 Three ____ with books? Yes, they're for Mrs. Nelson.
 a box
 b boxes
3 It's ____ small, blue bag.
 a an
 b a
4 Her ____ is green.
 a sweatshirts
 b sweatshirt
5 Sorry – no ____ in the classroom.
 a phone
 b phones
6 It isn't ____ coat.
 a an
 b a
7 Are you ____ architect?
 a an
 b a
8 All ____ are at nine o'clock.
 a classes
 b class
9 It's ____ orange book.
 a an
 b a
10 My glasses ____ black.
 a is
 b are

this, that, these, those

Choose the correct options to complete the sentences.

1 *This / That* is the classroom – our class is here.
2 *Are these / Is this* your bags?
3 Are *that / those* your glasses?
4 *This / These* isn't my hat. My hat's blue.
5 **A:** Is *that / those* your coat?
 B: No, *this / these* is my coat here.
6 *This / These* aren't good headphones.

PRONUNCIATION
/s/, /z/ and /ɪz/

A Practice saying the sentences aloud. Be careful with the underlined sounds.

1 Are these your umbrellas? /s/ /z/ /ɪz/
2 Those are cool hats. /s/ /z/ /ɪz/
3 When are your English classes? /s/ /z/ /ɪz/
4 These are good phones. /s/ /z/ /ɪz/
5 These aren't our coats. /s/ /z/ /ɪz/
6 Are those your glasses? /s/ /z/ /ɪz/

3.1 **B** Listen to the sentences from Exercise A. Then choose the correct sound for the underlined letters.

VOCABULARY
Family

A Look at the family tree. Complete the sentences with the words in the box.

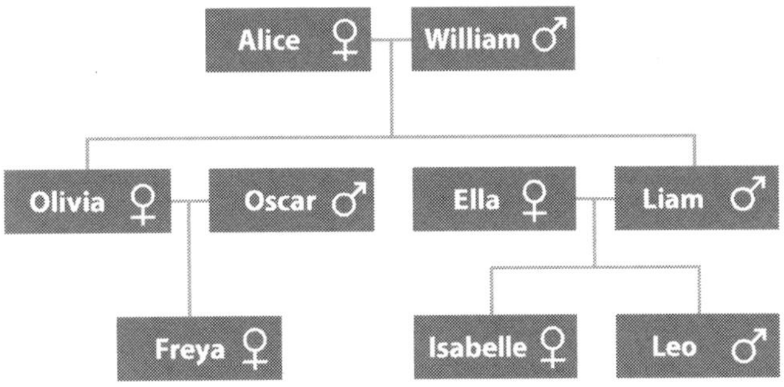

daughter grandfather grandparents grandson husband parents son wife

1 **Alice:** Liam is my ________.
2 **Oscar:** Olivia is my ________.
3 **Olivia:** Freya is my ________.
4 **Isabelle:** William is my ________.
5 **Leo:** Alice and William are my ________.
6 **Isabelle:** Ella and Liam are my ________.
7 **Alice:** William is my ________.
8 **William:** Leo is my ________.

B Choose the correct options to complete the sentences.

1 This is my *brother / grandfather*. He's younger than me.
2 **A:** How old is your *father / husband*?
B: He's 45 – the same as me.
3 David has two *sisters / mothers*, but he doesn't have any brothers.
4 My *daughter / grandmother* isn't at school today. She's at home.
5 **A:** How old is your *grandson / grandfather*?
B: He's 80.
6 These are my *wives / children* in this photo. Anna is seven and Rob is five.
7 My *parents / grandparents* are old – my mother is 75 and my father is 82.
8 There's a party to celebrate my *mother's / granddaughter's* birthday. She's four.

C Complete the text with the words in the box.

father grandmother grandparents mother sons wife's

My name's Jerry. I'm 40 years old. My [1] ________ name is Polly. She's 40, too. We have two children – two [2] ________ – and their names are Kevin and Peter. They don't have children, so we aren't [3] ________ – only parents!
My [4] ________ (our children's grandfather) is 65 years old and my [5] ________ is 64. I also have a [6] ________ (my father's mother). They all live in the same town as us, so that's good.

PRONUNCIATION
schwa /ə/

A Circle one word with the *schwa* sound in each group. Then listen and check.

1 party / people / mother
2 husband / grandchild / son
3 green / umbrella / women
4 children / headphones / sweatshirt
5 yellow / glasses / person
6 birthday / color / eighteen

B Listen and underline the *schwa* sounds.

1 This is my brother.
2 There's a party to celebrate.
3 My family lives here.
4 Lilly isn't the oldest person here.
5 Sally has two children.
6 She doesn't have a husband.

C Listen again and repeat.

GRAMMAR
have/has

A Complete the short conversations with the correct form of *have/has* or *do/does*.

Conversation 1

Tom: [1] __________ you [2] __________ a sister?
Lisa: Yes, I [3] __________. And you?
Tom: No, I [4] __________. I [5] __________ a brother.

Conversation 2

Said: Alex [1] __________ a green coat.
Kate: No, he [2] __________.
Said: Oh! [3] __________ he [4] __________ a black coat?
Kate: No, it isn't green or black. He [5] __________ a coat! He [6] __________ a sweatshirt!

Conversation 3

Heidi: This is a great photo – are these your children?
Jimmy: Yes, my wife and I [1] __________ two daughters. And you? Do you have children?
Heidi: Yes, we [2] __________. We [3] __________ a son, but we [4] __________ any daughters.

B Find and correct the mistakes with *have/has* or *do/does* in the sentences.

1 You have any brothers or sisters?
Do you have any brothers or sisters?
2 I haven't not a sister.
____
3 **A:** Do you have a car?
B: Yes, I've do.
____
4 We not have an umbrella.
____
5 You have a big coat?
____
6 Marc haven't a phone.
____
7 We's a class today.
____
8 Sam loves OneRepublic. He have all their CDs.
____

READING

A PREPARE TO READ Look at the title of the article and the picture. What do you think *surprise* means?

Surprise!

Today is Martha's birthday.

Martha comes from a big family. She has a brother and two sisters and they have their own children, too. Her parents are very happy to be grandparents and the family is always together on their birthdays. They all live in the same town, so it's easy to be together on special days.

This year, Martha has a new job in a big city. She's in New York now. At work, her colleagues say, 'Happy Birthday!' and give her a cake but it's not the same as when she's with her family.

Now she's at home, and … what's this? Her family is all here! Her mother and father, her brother and sisters and all their children, her grandparents, too – they're all here in her house! Surprise! It's a big party to celebrate Martha's birthday! There's a cake to eat and great music, too!

'I'm very lucky', says Martha. 'I have a very special family!' Happy Birthday, Martha!

B READ FOR GIST Read the article quickly. What is the surprise?

C READ FOR KEY INFORMATION Read the article again. Are the sentences true (T) or false (F)?

1 Martha has four brothers and sisters. T / F
2 Martha lives in the same town as her family. T / F
3 Martha's new home is in New York. T / F
4 Martha's family is at her house. T / F
5 There's pizza to eat. T / F

D REFLECT Think about the answers to these questions.

1 Is a surprise party fun? Why/Why not?
2 Do you celebrate your birthday with family, colleagues or friends?

LISTENING

A LISTEN FOR GIST (3.4) Listen to the conversation and answer the questions.

1 Where are the two women?
2 Who has a lot of new things – Naomi or Bahati?

B LISTEN FOR KEY WORDS (3.4) Listen and check (✓) the new things you hear the woman talk about.

1 a bag ☐
2 headphones ☐
3 glasses ☐
4 a phone ☐
5 a hat ☐
6 a coat ☐
7 a sweatshirt ☐

C LISTEN FOR DETAIL (3.4) Listen again. Match the phrases (1–5) with the objects (a–e).

1 a lot of	.....	a phone
2 blue	.....	b headphones
3 a super cool	.....	c glasses
4 a blue	.....	d sweatshirt
5 red	.....	e bags

D REFLECT Think about the answers to these questions.

1 Do you have these things in your bag – a phone, glasses, headphones, an umbrella?
2 What's your favorite color?

FUNCTIONAL LANGUAGE
Describing people

A Look at the pictures and complete the descriptions with the words in the box.

blond dark glasses long short

She has [1] ________ [2] ________ hair.

He has [3] ________ [4] ________ hair and [5] ________.

B Listen and complete the telephone conversation with one word in each blank.

Anna: Hello, Anna here.
Sally: Hi, Anna. This is Sally.
Anna: I'm [1] ________? Sally?
Sally: Yes. Carl's sister.
Anna: Oh, yes! Hi, Sally. How are you?
Sally: I'm fine, thanks. Look, I have your [2] ________. Do you want to meet? I can give it to you.
Anna: Yes. Thanks.
Sally: Um … [3] ________ you free at four o'clock?
Anna: Yes, I [4] ________.
Sally: Do you know Sam's Café?
Anna: Yes.
Sally: OK. See you there at four o'clock. Bye.
Anna: But, Sally!
Sally: Yes?
Anna: Do you have [5] ________ hair … long hair …?
Sally: Oh, yes, of course! I have short, light [6] ________ hair and … a red [7] ________.
Anna: OK. I have long black hair, a [8] ________ coat and a black scarf.

C 3.5 Listen again and label the pictures. Write *Sally* or *Anna*.

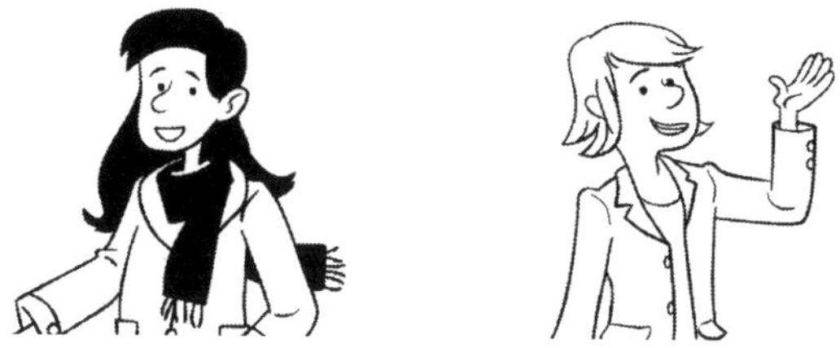

a ________ b ________

WRITING

A Look at the picture and read the social media post. Are the sentences true (T) or false (F)?

1 Tess is at her sister's house. T / F
2 Her brother isn't with them. T / F
3 Charlotte's husband's name is Tom. T / F
4 Charlotte's husband is in Peru. T / F

Tess Langdon
November 17th, 1 pm

It's Sunday and I'm free all day! I'm at my parents' house. My sisters, Charlotte and Miriam, are here. I have a brother, too. He isn't here. His name is Tom. On Sundays, we meet here to eat and talk. I'm the one with long dark hair next to my dad. He has gray hair and a beard. The man next to me is my sister Charlotte's husband, Gerald. Miriam has a husband, but he's in Peru. My parents are happy we're here.

6 25 8

B **USING *BUT*** Read the post again. Find two sentences which can be joined with *but*. Rewrite them as one sentence.

WRITING PRACTICE

WRITE Look at the picture. Imagine you are at work and it is your birthday. Write a social media post about this special day. Use Tess's post to help you. Do not forget to use *but* to join different ideas.

VOCABULARY
Daily activities

Complete the text with the verbs in the box.

finish get go (x4) have read talk watch

My day starts when I [1] ______________ up at seven o'clock in the morning. I [2] ______________ breakfast and I [3] ______________ to work at eight. I [4] ______________ work at four in the afternoon, and then I [5] ______________ home and [6] ______________ to my family. In the evenings, I [7] ______________ out with my friends, or I [8] ______________ a book or [9] ______________ a movie. I [10] ______________ to bed at 11:30 at night.

Time

A Match the sentences (1–8) with the times (a–h).

1 I have breakfast at six thirty in the morning. ____
2 I go to work at seven o'clock in the morning. ____
3 I finish work at five ten in the afternoon. ____
4 I watch TV at eight thirty in the evening. ____
5 I go home at six fifty in the evening. ____
6 I go out at nine fifteen in the evening. ____
7 I have a class at eight forty-five in the morning. ____
8 I go to bed at twelve o'clock at night. ____

a 12 am
b 5:10 pm
c 8:45 am
d 8:30 pm
e 9:15 pm
f 6:50 pm
g 6:30 am
h 7 am

B Draw the times on the clocks.

a one o'clock

b three fifteen

c four fifty

d eleven thirty

e nine forty-five

f three forty

g six twenty-five

h eleven fifty-five

i eight thirty-five

j seven oh five

GRAMMAR
Simple present: *I*, *you*, *we*, *they*

A Complete the sentences with a verb in the simple present.

1 I don't work on a big team. I ___work___ on a small team.
2 We don't live in different towns. We ________ in the same town.
3 They don't go to work at seven o'clock. They ________ to work at eight o'clock.
4 You go out in the evening. You ________ out in the morning.
5 We don't finish work at six. We ________ work at five thirty.
6 They read emails. They ________ books.
7 I go to work in the morning. I ________ to work at night.
8 You live in New York. You ________ here.

B Reorder the words to make sentences.

1 relax / in the evenings / We
________.
2 live / I / in a lighthouse / don't
________.
3 work / You / in a school
________.
4 on the computer / don't / We / play games
________.
5 don't / I / on Mondays / go out
________.
6 don't / about work / They / talk
________.
7 finish / work / We / at six thirty
________.
8 get up early / don't / on Sundays / They
________.

PRONUNCIATION
Sentence stress

4.1 **A Underline the stressed words in the sentences. Then listen and check.**

1 I get up at seven o'clock.
2 I have breakfast at home.
3 I go to work at eight in the morning.
4 I finish work at six thirty.
5 I don't go out in the evenings – I read or watch TV.
6 I go to bed at 11 o'clock.

4.2 **B Listen and complete the sentences.**

1 They ________ in a ________.
2 We have ________ ________ every ________.
3 You ________ start ________ until ________ o'clock in the ________.
4 They teach ________ in ________.
5 We ________ ________ at ________ o'clock in the ________.
6 The ________ ________ watch ________ in the morning.

VOCABULARY
Months and seasons

A Complete the sequences with the correct months of the year.

1 January, February, ________________
2 September, ________________, November
3 ________________, July, August
4 March, April, ________________
5 August, ________________, October
6 November, December, ________________

B Look at the table and choose the correct options to complete the sentences.

The seasons in Poland		The seasons in Argentina
spring	March	fall
	April	
	May	
summer	June	winter
	July	
	August	
fall	September	spring
	October	
	November	
winter	December	summer
	January	
	February	

1 In Poland, the spring starts in ***March / September***.
2 December, January and February are ***summer / winter*** months in Poland.
3 The Polish ***spring / summer*** is in June, July and August.
4 Winter starts in ***June / December*** in Argentina.
5 In September, it is ***fall / spring*** in Argentina.
6 The ***winter / summer*** months in Argentina are December, January and February.

C Complete the text with one word in each blank. The first two letters are given to help you.

I'm Georgia and I'm from Greece. My favorite season is [1]su________________. The sun is nice (take sunglasses!). Children don't go to school, but I go to work. The hot months are July and [2]Au________________. It's nice in the [3]fa________________, too – I like September and [4]Oc________________.

Greece is cold in the [5]wi________________. You need a hat and coat! January and [6]Fe________________ are cold months. But the [7]sp________________ is nice – in March and [8]Ap________________, we go to the countryside.

GRAMMAR
Simple present questions: *I, you, we, they*

A Choose the correct options (a, b or c) to answer the questions.

1 Do you live here?
 a Yes, I live.
 b No, I don't.
 c No, I don't live.
2 When do you go to work?
 a Yes, I do.
 b By car.
 c At seven thirty.
3 Do you have a favorite season?
 a Yes, I do. It's spring.
 b In the spring.
 c Yes, I have spring.
4 Do you go to another country in the summer?
 a No, I don't go.
 b Yes, I go.
 c Yes, I do.
5 Who do you live with?
 a Yes, I live with my wife.
 b My wife.
 c Yes, I live with.
6 Do you both live in Switzerland?
 a Yes, we live.
 b Yes, it is.
 c Yes, we do.
7 When do you finish work?
 a At six o'clock.
 b Yes, I do.
 c I go home.
8 Do your friends live in the same town?
 a No, we don't.
 b No, they don't.
 c No, you don't.
9 Do you two work for the same company?
 a Yes, you do.
 b Yes, they do.
 c Yes, we do.
10 Do you like your colleagues?
 a Yes, you do.
 b Yes, they are.
 c Yes, I do.

B Read the answers and complete the questions.

1 **A:** Where ________________ live?
 B: I live in La Plata.
2 **A:** Do ________________ here?
 B: No, I don't. I work in Buenos Aires.
3 **A:** When ________________ in the morning?
 B: I get up at six.
4 **A:** Do ________________ late?
 B: Yes, they do. They go to bed at two in the morning.
5 **A:** Who ________________ work with?
 B: I work with Frank and Josephine.
6 **A:** Do ________________ breakfast in the morning?
 B: Yes, I do. I have breakfast when I get up.

PRONUNCIATION
Do you /ʤʊ/

4.3 **A** Listen to the questions and check (✓) the questions where the speaker says /ʤʊ/.

1 Where do you live? ☐
2 Do you work in the town center? ☐
3 What time do you finish work? ☐
4 Do you go out in the evenings? ☐
5 What do you do in the winter? ☐
6 Do you live in the countryside? ☐
7 Who do you work with? ☐
8 Do you go to bed late? ☐

4.3 **B** Listen again and repeat the questions.

READING

A USE PICTURES BEFORE YOU READ Look at the picture in the blog post. Is this place hot or cold?

B READ FOR GIST Read the blog post and check your answer to Exercise A.

Susie's blog of interesting places around the world!

Do you think it's cold in your town in the winter? Read about a very, very cold town.

Oymyakon is in northern Russia and in the winter it's -50° Celsius! In this part of the world, it's always dark in the winter – in December, the day is just three hours long. But the summer is very different. It's nice and light and the day is 21 hours long! How do they know when to go to bed?

Oymyakon isn't a big place. There are 500 people in the town and they live in small houses. There's a school and a store. Some people are teachers, and there are engineers and builders, too, but life is very difficult for people in the winter. They don't go out a lot because it's very cold! But guess what? Some tourists go to Oymyakon – yes! They want to know about life in this very cold place.

C READ FOR DETAIL Read the blog post again. Choose the correct options to complete the sentences.

1 Oymyakon is in …
   a northern Russia. **b** southern Russia.
2 It is -50° Celsius …
   a in the winter. **b** in the summer.
3 In the summer, the day is …
   a 3 hours long. **b** 21 hours long.
4 The people of Oymyakon live in …
   a big houses. **b** small houses.
5 Life isn't …
   a easy. **b** difficult.

D REFLECT Think about the answers to these questions.

1 Would you like to go to Oymyakon?
2 Do you like the winter?

LISTENING

A PREPARE TO LISTEN Read the notes in Exercise C. Which picture shows Keith's job?

a

b

4.4 **B LISTEN FOR MAIN IDEA** Listen to a conversation and choose the correct options to complete the sentences.

1 This conversation is *in a café* / *on the radio*.
2 It's about *daily routines* / *jobs*.
3 Keith *has* / *doesn't have* friends.

4.4 **C LISTEN FOR DETAIL** Listen again and complete the notes with one word or number in each blank.

Day by day: Keith Hatfield

Madeira to [1] ____________ *Restaurant – Spanish and* [2] ____________ *food*

- *go to work –* [3] ____________ *in the morning*
- *have* [4] ____________ *at the restaurant*
- [5] ____________ *work – three o'clock*
- *take a* [6] ____________ *in the afternoon*

D REFLECT Think about the answers to these questions.

1 Is it good to start work very early like Keith? Why/Why not?
2 Do you sometimes sleep in the afternoon?

FUNCTIONAL LANGUAGE

Ordering in a café

A Complete the conversation with the phrases in the box.

Can I have	do you want	large	please
Small	Sorry	To go	What can I get you

A: Hello.

B: Good afternoon. [1] ________________?

A: [2] ________________ a cappuccino … no … a tea, please?

B: Of course. [3] ________________, medium or [4] ________________?

A: Medium, please. [5] ________________.

B: And [6] ________________ milk with that?

A: Yes, [7] ________________. Can I have a croissant, too?

B: [8] ________________, we don't have any croissants today.

A: Oh OK. Just the tea then.

B: Here you are.

A: Thanks. Bye!

B Listen and check your ideas from Exercise A.

WRITING

A Look at the picture and read the email. When does Dev do the following activities? Write a time or a part of the day, e.g. *five o'clock*, *morning*, etc.

1 read a book ________________
2 finish work ________________
3 get up ________________
4 call brother ________________
5 go to bed ________________
6 have dinner ________________

Hi Roberto,

How are you? I am fine. I have a new job! I am a postman now.

I get up at six o'clock in the morning, have breakfast and walk to work. I do not have a car. It is nice to work in the summer months. I finish work at one or two o'clock in the afternoon. It is not a long day. I go home and have lunch. And my wife, Gretel? She is at work in the afternoon, so I read a book or watch TV. In the evening, we have dinner at seven o'clock. I talk to my brother or my parents on the phone. We go to bed at nine or ten o'clock.

What about you? What is your routine?

Dev

P.S. Here is a photo of me doing my new job.

B USING CONTRACTIONS Rewrite the email using contractions.

WRITING PRACTICE

WRITE Write an email to a friend about your routine on a day when you do not work. Use Dev's email to help you. Do not forget to use contractions.

5.1 Time for a break

VOCABULARY
Free-time activities

A Choose the correct options (a, b or c) to complete the sentences.

1 On Sundays, I ___ for a walk after lunch.
  a go　b have　c play
2 My grandparents just ___ in the backyard all day!
  a cook　b go　c sit
3 I'm so busy that I don't have time to ___ a meal.
  a cook　b play　c sit
4 I like to ___ a bath in the evening.
  a go　b take　c play
5 Do you want to ___ shopping after work?
  a go　b have　c play
6 They ___ to the gym three times a week.
  a go　b play　c sit

B Complete the text with one word in each blank. The first letter is given to help you.

I work a lot from Monday to Friday, so when the weekend is here, I like to relax! On Saturday morning, I get up late and take a long 1b__________ because I have a lot of time. Then, I go for a 2w__________ in the countryside, or I go 3s__________ in town. In the evening, I meet my friend Robert and we play 4c__________, or we go out somewhere. On Sunday, I cook a 5m__________ for my friends. We talk or we sit in the 6b__________. I don't go 7r__________ or to the 8g__________ – that's not relaxing for me!

C Find and correct the mistakes in six of the sentences.

1 When it's a nice day, we sit at the backyard.
____
2 Do you want to go for running tomorrow?
____
3 In the evenings, I take a bath before I go to bed.
____
4 Do they go the gym every day?
____
5 In the afternoons, we play at chess.
____
6 On Saturdays, I go for shopping.
____
7 I cook a meal for my family on Sundays.
____
8 Why don't we go a walk in the park?
____

GRAMMAR
Simple present: *he, she, it*

A Choose the correct options (a, b or c) to complete the sentences.

1 Paolo ___ for a walk every morning.
  a go
  b goes
  c he goes
2 ___ in town?
  a Lee works
  b Does Lee she work
  c Does Lee work
3 He ___ chess.
  a doesn't play
  b not plays
  c doesn't plays
4 **A:** Who ___ your laundry for you?
  B: I do!
  a do
  b does do
  c does
5 **A:** Does Ian relax on the weekends?
  B: Yes, he ___.
  a does
  b relax
  c does relax
6 What ___ on Saturdays?
  a does Fran do
  b does Fran
  c Fran does
7 Tina ___ TV every evening.
  a watch
  b watches
  c watchs
8 Where ___?
  a does Hercules work
  b works Hercules
  c does Hercules works
9 **A:** Does Marcus go to the gym every day?
  B: No, ___.
  a doesn't he
  b he doesn't
  c he doesn't go
10 ___ every Sunday evening.
  a Does Maria take a bath
  b Maria does a bath
  c Maria takes a bath

B Complete the conversation with the correct forms of the verbs in parentheses or the correct short answer.

Noah: [1] ___ (*your parents / live*) in the same town as you?
Angie: Yes, [2] ___. They live about five minutes from my house.
Noah: So, do you see them regularly?
Angie: Yes, I see them every week. I go shopping with my mom every Saturday, and my dad [3] ___ (*cook*) a meal for us all – my mom [4] ___ (*not* cook)! What about your parents? Do your parents live here?
Noah: No, [5] ___.
Angie: How far from you [6] ___ (*they / live*)?
Noah: They live very far away. And they don't have a car, so they [7] ___ (*not come*) to see me – I go to see them. It's about three hours from here. But we talk a lot.
Angie: How do you talk to them?
Noah: I call them – and my mom [8] ___ (*use*) the internet to talk to me.

PRONUNCIATION
does he / does she

5.1 **A** Listen and complete the questions with *he* or *she*.

1 Does ___ live in the same town as you?
2 Where does ___ work?
3 What does ___ want to do?
4 Does ___ usually go running?
5 How does ___ go to work in the morning?
6 What kind of food does ___ like?
7 Does ___ play chess?
8 What does ___ do to relax on the weekends?

5.1 **B** Listen again to the questions from Exercise A. Practice asking the questions.

VOCABULARY

Food and meals

A Choose the correct options to complete the text.

A good day for me starts with a nice healthy breakfast. It's OK to have only a piece of [1]***bread / chips*** and some milk or [2]***juice / rice***, but when I'm really hungry, I have [3]***water / eggs***, too!

For lunch and dinner, I don't eat a lot of meat – maybe a little [4]***tea / chicken***. I cook that with [5]***potatoes / fruit*** and beans, sometimes in a tomato sauce. I eat [6]***fish / cookies*** – that's very good for your health. But I don't eat meat or fish every day. I like pasta – my favorite is [7]***apples / macaroni***. Sometimes I cook [8]***drinks / rice*** with vegetables. I put [9]***cheese / snacks*** on top when it's hot – that's my favorite meal when I'm hungry!

And finally, I don't eat snacks like chips or cookies. I prefer a piece of fruit like a(n) [10]***chocolate / apple*** or a banana. I think that's a good way to stay healthy!

B Complete the table with the words in the box.

broccoli chips cookies cucumber grapes juice milk onion orange peanuts pear water

Fruits	Vegetables	Drinks	Snacks
banana	tomato	tea	chocolate

GRAMMAR
Adverbs of frequency

A Rewrite the sentences with one adverb of frequency from the box in the right place. Sometimes more than one option is possible.

always	frequently	never	sometimes	usually

1 I eat chicken because I don't like it.

....

2 Most nights, I go to bed early. I'm in bed by 10 o'clock.

....

3 I eat fish because it's good for my health – but only once a month.

....

4 I'm at the gym after work – I go every day of the week.

....

5 I sometimes run to work (about once a week), but I walk (about four times a week).

....

B Find and correct the mistakes with adverbs of frequency in the sentences.

1 Jim eats frequently eggs.

....

2 We eat never late at night.

....

3 We eat sometimes lunch in a restaurant.

....

4 We always are busy on the weekends.

....

5 Ken doesn't never drink milk.

....

6 I always am late for work!

....

7 I have usually a salad for lunch.

....

8 They don't have usually breakfast.

....

PRONUNCIATION
Linking with /j/

5.2 **A** Draw a ‿ to show the words that are linked with a /j/ sound. Then listen and check.

1 She eats a lot of salad.
2 I often have eggs for breakfast.
3 The oranges are nice.
4 What does he eat for breakfast?
5 Tea is my favorite drink.
6 We often eat at home.
7 He always drinks coffee before work.

5.2 **B** Practice saying the sentences in Exercise A.

C Some of the underlined letters are linked with a /j/ sound. Follow the phrases which are connected with a /j/ sound to get out of the maze.

READING

A SKIM Read *Breakfasts around the world* and answer the questions.

1 How many countries are mentioned in the text?
2 Which country's breakfast can you see in the picture?

BREAKFASTS around the world

Do you start the day with a good breakfast, or do you usually drink a cup of coffee and quickly leave the house? There are many kinds of breakfast in different countries around the world.

Germany

In Germany, people like to have different kinds of freshly cooked bread for breakfast. They like white and brown bread. They eat it with cheese or cold meat, and many people have eggs, too. Some people also eat cereal with milk and fruit. They always drink a lot of strong coffee.

Mexico

Here people frequently have a big breakfast. Their favorite breakfast dish is called *huevos rancheros.* People have a type of bread called *tortillas* which they fill with **eggs** and beans and a sauce with tomatoes and onions. They usually drink coffee with a lot of sugar and milk, and some people have hot chocolate.

Japan

Japanese people often have rice for breakfast. It can be white or brown. Sometimes they like to have a soup with beans, vegetables and fish. Another breakfast food is called *tamago kake gohan.* This is rice with an egg – but they don't cook the egg! Japanese people usually drink green tea with their breakfast.

B READ FOR DETAIL Read the blog post again. Are the sentences true (T) or false (F)?

1 In Germany, people only eat white bread. *T / F*
2 People never eat eggs for breakfast in Germany. *T / F*
3 Mexicans like to eat a big breakfast. *T / F*
4 Mexicans like sweet drinks with their breakfast. *T / F*
5 Japanese people don't like soup for breakfast. *T / F*
6 Coffee is Japanese people's favorite drink. *T / F*

C REFLECT Think about the answers to these questions.

1 Which of the breakfasts in the blog post do you like? Why?
2 What do you have for breakfast?

LISTENING

5.3 **A LISTEN FOR GIST** Listen to the first part of a conversation and label the people in the picture. Write *Wendy* or *Mrs. Turner.*

5.4 **B LISTEN FOR GIST** Listen to the rest of the conversation and choose the correct options to answer the questions.

1 Who is Mrs. Turner?
 a a family friend b Sam's mother
2 Where does Sam like to play?
 a at home b in the park
3 Which meals will Sam have with Wendy?
 a breakfast and lunch b breakfast

5.4 **C LISTEN FOR DETAIL** Listen again and complete the sentences with one to three words in each blank.

1 For breakfast, Sam has ____________ with milk.
2 He goes to the park and ____________ with his ball.
3 Sam's coat is ____________.
4 He wears a ____________ when it's cold.
5 Sam likes ____________ for lunch.
6 He ____________ juice.
7 In the afternoon, he takes a nap for ____________.
8 Mrs. Turner usually comes home from work at ____________.

D REFLECT Think about the answers to these questions.

1 Is it good for children to take a nap in the afternoon? Why/Why not?
2 What are some healthy foods for children?

5.4 Time for a break

Functional Language; Write a blog about food

FUNCTIONAL LANGUAGE

Asking for information

A Reorder the words to make sentences and questions.

1. does / it / long / How / take
   ______________________________?
2. ticket / How / is / much / a / round-trip
   ______________________________?
3. to / like / please / a ticket / I'd / Rye,
   ______________________________.
4. leave / time / it / does / What
   ______________________________?

B Read the information in the timetable. Then complete the conversation with the sentences from Exercise A.

Departure	From	To	Arrival	Time	One-way	Round-trip
11:30	Milford	Rye	1:30	2 hrs	$54	$102

Ticket seller: Can I help you?
Customer: 1 ______________________________
Ticket seller: That's $54 for a one-way ticket.
Customer: 2 ______________________________
Ticket seller: 11:30.
Customer: 3 ______________________________
Ticket seller: About two hours.
Customer: 4 ______________________________
Ticket seller: $102.
Customer: Wow! That's expensive. A one-way ticket to Rye, please.

.5 **C** Listen to the conversation and check your answers to Exercise B.

WRITING

A Read Sal's blog and choose the correct options to complete the sentences.

1. Sal works in *an office* / *a restaurant*.
2. She *never* / *usually* has a salad for lunch.
3. *Her sister eats* / *Her colleagues eat* at a restaurant every day.
4. She *sometimes* / *never* goes to the restaurant with her colleagues.

SAL'S FOOD BLOG

I usually eat my lunch in the office. I bring a salad from home and I eat [1]the salad at my desk. My sister lives near the office and sometimes I meet [2]my sister for lunch at a restaurant. Some of my colleagues eat at a restaurant every day. [3]My colleagues usually go to an Italian restaurant near the office where [4]my colleagues and I work. Once a week, I go with [5]my colleagues to the restaurant. They usually eat pasta with meat or chicken, but I often have fresh fish – my favorite. We usually share a big salad. I like it when we all eat together.

B **USING PRONOUNS** Read the blog again and replace the underlined words with object or subject pronouns.

WRITING PRACTICE

A **PLAN** You are going to write a blog about a meal when all of your family gets together. Write some notes about:

- what you usually eat
- where you usually eat
- who you usually eat with

B **WRITE** Write your blog post. Use Sal's blog to help you. Remember to use object pronouns.

VOCABULARY
Places in a town

A Complete the crossword.

Across

5 I like to go to the art ________ to look at the paintings.

6 This is a great ________ to buy clothes.

8 Sometimes I don't cook and I eat in a ________.

Down

1 We stay in a ________ when we're on vacation.

2 The children play in the ________.

3 To learn about the history of the town, go to the ________.

4 You find fresh fruits and vegetables at the farmers' ________.

6 At seven o'clock, Jack goes to the ________ to get the train to work.

7 We go to the ________ to get a drink and a snack.

9 Let's go to see a play at the ________.

B Complete the text with words from Exercise A.

MY WORK DAY

Every morning, I get up early and walk to the 1 ________ and get the train to my office in the city. It's nice because I walk in the 2 ________. There aren't any children there in the early morning and it's very quiet. When I'm not late, I sometimes have a cup of coffee at the 3 ________ in the station and wait for my train there. For my lunch break, I sometimes go to the art 4 ________ to look at the paintings. I often meet customers and take them for lunch at a 5 ________ near my office. In the evening, after work, I sometimes go to the 6 ________ to see a play. Most afternoons, I take the train home, but I usually walk through the town. I often go to the farmers' 7 ________ to get some fruits and vegetables, and sometimes I look at clothes in the 8 ________ in town, but I don't usually buy things.

6.1 A place to live

GRAMMAR
there is / there are; *some* and *any*

A Choose the correct options to complete the sentences.

1 There ___ a nice park near my house.
  a 's
  b are
2 There aren't ___ museums in my town.
  a any
  b some
3 There ___ a lot of theaters in the city.
  a 's
  b are
4 There ___ a produce market here.
  a aren't
  b isn't
5 There are ___ stores in my town.
  a any
  b some
6 There ___ apples at the market.
  a aren't any
  b isn't some
7 There ___ an art gallery here.
  a doesn't
  b isn't
8 **A:** Where are you? What's near you?
  B: ___ a station here. And a theater – the Apollo.
  a There's
  b There are
9 There ___ hotels in my town.
  a isn't a
  b aren't any
10 There are ___ really cheap vegetables at the market today.
  a some
  b any
11 **A:** Excuse me, where's the bank?
  B: Sorry, there ___.
  a isn't a bank near here.
  b isn't any bank near here.
12 That's unusual. There ___ children in the park this afternoon.
  a isn't any
  b aren't any

B Match the beginnings of the sentences (1–6) with the endings (a–f).

1 There are some ___
2 There aren't a ___
3 There's a ___
4 There isn't a ___
5 There are a lot of men in my class, but there's ___
6 My work isn't easy. There are ___

a only one woman.
b great café near my office. I go there every day.
c a lot of problems.
d lot of restaurants here, so we go into the city.
e bank here – sorry.
f great paintings in the gallery.

PRONUNCIATION
there is / there are

A Read the text. How would you pronounce *there is* and *there are*?

There are a lot of small stores in my town. There's a large grocery store, too. There's a café in the park and there's a train station. There's a museum, but there aren't any theaters. There's an art gallery and there are two hotels.

6.1 **B** Listen to the text in Exercise A. Then repeat.

6.2 A place to live

VOCABULARY

Furniture and rooms

Look at the pictures and label the furniture and the rooms.

a ____________ b ____________ c ____________

1 ____________
2 ____________
3 ____________
4 ____________
5 ____________
6 ____________
7 ____________
8 ____________

Prepositions of place

Choose the correct options to complete the text.

The perfect room for a student

There's a desk, a chair and a bed [1]***in* / *on*** this room. The desk is [2]***under* / *in*** the window, so there's more light in the day, but there are also lamps [3]***in* / *on*** the desk and bookshelf. There are two bookshelves and a clock [4]***under* / *on*** the wall. There's a shower and a toilet [5]***in* / *on*** the room, too.

GRAMMAR

is there / are there question forms

A Read the answers and complete the questions.

1 ________________ a theater in the town?
Yes, there is. We frequently watch plays there.

2 ________________ any bananas in the fridge?
No, there aren't. Sorry!

3 ________________ a clock on the wall?
No there isn't, but there's a bookshelf.

4 ________________ any furniture in the room?
Yes, there's a bed, a desk and a chair.

5 ________________ any things in the closet?
Yes, there are. There are some clothes and books.

6 ________________ a mirror in the bathroom?
No, there isn't. But there's one in my bedroom.

B Complete the short conversations with *Is there, Are there* or short answers.

A: 1 ________________ a bathroom here?
B: Yes, 2 ________________.

A: 3 ________________ any stores near your house?
B: No, 4 ________________.

A: 5 ________________ a living room in your apartment?
B: Yes, of course there is – and 6 ________________ three bedrooms.

A: 7 ________________ a lot of books in the student's room?
B: No, 8 ________________.

A: 9 ________________ any milk in the fridge?
B: Yes, 10 ________________.

A: 11 ________________ a lot of people in your class?
B: No, 12 ________________. It's just me and three other people.

PRONUNCIATION

Vowel sounds: /ʌ/ and /e/

A Practice reading the pairs of sentences aloud.

1 a There's a hat on his head.
b There's a hat on his bed.

2 a There are some rugs in the apartment.
b There are some bags in the apartment.

3 a The pen is red.
b The pan is red.

4 a He runs to work at seven.
b He gets to work at seven.

5 a There's some bread in the kitchen.
b There's an onion in the kitchen.

6.2 **B** Read the sentences in Exercise A again. Listen and circle the sentence you hear.

6.3 **C** Listen and choose the correct sound for each word.

1	rug	/ʌ/	/e/
2	run	/ʌ/	/e/
3	ten	/ʌ/	/e/
4	cup	/ʌ/	/e/
5	them	/ʌ/	/e/
6	lunch	/ʌ/	/e/
7	tent	/ʌ/	/e/
8	month	/ʌ/	/e/

6.4 **D** Cross out the word in each group with a different vowel sound. Then listen and check.

1	rug	some	bread
2	get	run	desk
3	bus	rent	ten
4	cup	fun	bed
5	lunch	them	nuts
6	mom	son	done
7	tent	sun	one
8	month	let	but

READING

A PREPARE TO READ Look at the pictures in *The Athens of the north*. What is similar about them?

B READ FOR GIST Read the blog post. Number the places (a–d) in the order you read about them (1–4).

a restaurants ____ **c** castle ____
b park ____ **d** art gallery ____

C READ FOR DETAIL Read the blog post again and choose the correct options to complete the sentences.

1 The writer is on vacation in *Scotland / Greece*.
2 At Edinburgh Castle, you can *learn about history / read stories*.
3 The Castle is usually *quiet / busy*.
4 It's *not far / far* from Princes Street Gardens to the station.
5 The writer *doesn't enjoy / enjoys* looking at paintings.
6 The writer likes 'Café Martone' because it has *a good view / delicious food*.

D REFLECT Think about the answers to these questions.

1 Would you like to visit Edinburgh? Why/Why not?
2 What do you like to see when you're on vacation – castles, museums, art galleries or something else?

About Profile **Blog** Contact

The Athens of the North

Athens, Greece

Edinburgh, Scotland

Hi guys. Today's blog post is a bit different because . . . I'm on vacation! Yes, this weekend, I'm in Edinburgh. It's Scotland's first city, and it's sometimes called 'the Athens of the North' because its beautiful buildings look like they are from ancient Greece.

High above the city is Edinburgh Castle – it's like something out of a story book! There are different museums *inside* the castle and you can learn all about the history of the city and the area. But get there early because there are a lot of tourists and sometimes there's a long line for tickets.

You can drive to Edinburgh or you can take the train. There's a big train station right in the city center. Near the station is a beautiful park called Princes Street Gardens with trees and flowers. People walk there and enjoy the sun on warm days.

There are a lot of art galleries in Edinburgh, but I think the best one is the Scottish National Gallery. They have hundreds of beautiful paintings – some old and some modern. It's a great place.

And what about food? Choose from cool little cafés for coffee and cake, cheap street food, traditional Scottish food or cool, modern restaurants with international menus. Right now, I'm in an Italian place called 'Café Martone'. From here I can see the castle. It looks amazing!

LISTENING

6.5 **A LISTEN FOR GIST** Listen to a conversation in a furniture store and choose the correct options to complete the sentences.

1 *There's / There isn't* any furniture in William's new apartment.
2 William *has / doesn't have* a lot of money.
3 William buys *a bed, a desk and a chair / a bed, a desk, a chair and a bookshelf*.

B PREDICT Read William's letter to his parents in Exercise C. Predict which of these topics (a–e) will go in each blank.

a a price ____
b an apartment number ____
c a color ____
d a place ____
e an object ____

6.5 **C LISTEN FOR DETAIL** Listen to the conversation again and complete William's letter to his parents with a word or number in each blank.

Hi Mom and Dad!

How are you? I'm fine. I love it here in Toronto! My classes are a little difficult, but my new friends are great. I have some new furniture for the studio [1] ____________! Yay! First – a new bed. It isn't blue. It's [2] ____________, but that's OK. I also have a desk – a nice big one. $[3] ____________ with a new chair, too! That's a good price, right? I don't have a [4] ____________. Can you bring me one from home?

My new address is Apartment 4b, [5] ____________ West Street. Write soon!

Love,

William

D REFLECT Think about the answers to these questions.

1 Is furniture expensive in your country?
2 Do students in your country usually live in an apartment or with their family?

FUNCTIONAL LANGUAGE

Asking for and giving directions

A Look at the map and follow these directions. Where are you?

Go out of the café and turn right. Then turn left. The library is on your right. Go straight ahead, past the hotel and it's on your left.

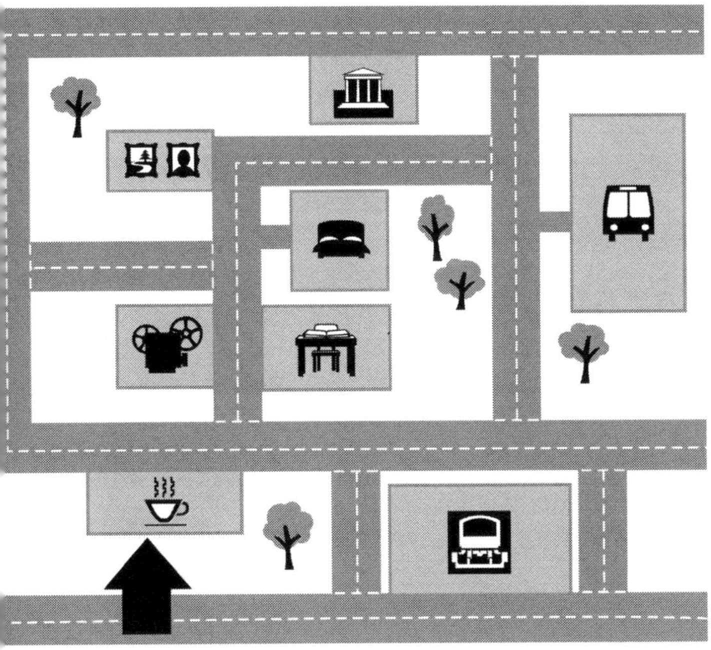

B Complete the conversation with the missing directions. Use the map above to help you.

Woman: Excuse me. Is the museum near here?

Helen: The museum? Let me see. Oh … I'm not sure.

Jimmy: It's OK. I can tell you. It's not very far. Go out of the café.[1] ________ right, then [2] ________ left. The museum is [3] ________ your left.

Gilbert: No, that's the [4] ________.

Jimmy: The movie theater's on the right, not the left.

Gilbert: No. The [5] ________ is on the right. The movie theater is on the left.

Helen: OK, everybody. Let's just relax, OK?

Roberto: Yes, calm down, everybody! Jimmy, Gilbert – you're both wrong. To get to the museum, you go out of the café, turn right, then left, then right, then left, then left again and the museum's on your [6] ________.

Woman: Ah! Thank you.

C Now listen and check your answers to Exercise B.

.6

WRITING

A Read the review. Why does the writer like the café?

Fantastic croissants!

I love this café because everyone here is friendly and it's super cool! It's usually very busy in the morning when people go to work, but I come here at about 11 o'clock, so I don't have to wait for my coffee and fresh croissant. The coffee is expensive, but it's excellent and I always have a croissant because they are delicious here. The music they play is really good and there's free wi-fi, too, so bring your computer!

B Read the review again. Are the sentences true (T) or false (F)?

1. The people at the café are friendly. *T / F*
2. It's usually busy at 11 o'clock. *T / F*
3. The croissants are good, but the coffee isn't. *T / F*
4. The writer likes the music at the café. *T / F*

C **USING *BECAUSE*** Match the sentence beginnings (1–5) to the sentence endings (a–e).

1. I always drink tea because
2. We don't go to that café because
3. That café has a lot of customers because
4. She always takes her computer because
5. The snacks aren't nice because

a it's cheap.
b I don't like coffee.
c they're not fresh.
d the people aren't friendly.
e there's free wi-fi.

WRITING PRACTICE

A **PLAN** You are going to write a review of a café that you *do not* like. Write notes on what you do not like and why.

B **WRITE** Write a review of your café. Remember to use *because* to give reasons.

Irregular Verbs

Base form	Simple past	Past participle
be	was/were	been
become	became	become
begin	began	begun
break	broke	broken
bring	brought	brought
build	built	built
buy	bought	bought
can	could	been able to
catch	caught	caught
choose	chose	chosen
come	came	come
cost	cost	cost
cut	cut	cut
drink	drank	drunk
eat	ate	eaten
fall	fell	fallen
feel	felt	felt
find	found	found
forget	forgot	forgotten
get	got	got
give	gave	given
go	went	gone/been
grow	grew	grown
have	had	had
hear	heard	heard
hit	hit	hit
hold	held	held
hurt	hurt	hurt
keep	kept	kept
know	knew	known
leave	left	left
lend	lent	lent
let	let	let

Base form	Simple past	Past participle
lose	lost	lost
make	made	made
mean	meant	meant
meet	met	met
must	had to	had to
pay	paid	paid
put	put	put
read	read	read
ride	rode	ridden
run	ran	run
say	said	said
see	saw	seen
sell	sold	sold
send	sent	sent
set	set	set
shut	shut	shut
sing	sang	sung
sit	sat	sat
sleep	slept	slept
speak	spoke	spoken
spell	spelled	spelled
spend	spent	spent
stand	stood	stood
steal	stole	stolen
take	took	taken
teach	taught	taught
tell	told	told
think	thought	thought
throw	threw	thrown
understand	understood	understood
wear	wore	worn
win	won	won
write	wrote	written

PHONETIC SYMBOLS											
Single vowels			Diphthongs			Consonants					
/ɪ/	fish	/fɪʃ/	/uw/	news	/nuw/	/p/	pen	/pen/	/s/	snake	/sneɪk/
/iː/	bean	/biːn/	/eɪ/	face	/feɪs/	/b/	bag	/bæg/	/z/	zoo	/zuː/
/ʊ/	foot	/fʊt/	/ɔɪ/	boy	/bɔɪ/	/t/	tea	/tiː/	/ʃ/	shop	/ʃɒp/
/uː/	shoe	/ʃuː/	/oʊ/	nose	/noʊz/	/d/	dog	/dɒg/	/ʒ/	television	/'telɪvɪʒən/
/e/	egg	/eg/	/ju/	use	/juz/	/ʧ/	chip	/ʧɪp/	/m/	map	/mæp/
/ə/	mother	/'mʌðər/	/aɪ/	eye	/aɪ/	/ʤ/	jazz	/ʤæz/	/n/	name	/neɪm/
/ɜː/	word	/wɜːrd/	/aʊ/	mouth	/maʊθ/	/k/	cake	/keɪk/	/ŋ/	ring	/rɪŋ/
/ɔː/	talk	/tɔːk/				/g/	girl	/gɜːrl/	/h/	house	/haʊs/
/æ/	back	/bæk/				/f/	film	/fɪlm/	/l/	leg	/leg/
/ʌ/	bus	/bʌs/				/v/	verb	/vɜːrb/	/r/	road	/roʊd/
/ɑː/	arm	/ɑːrm/				/θ/	thing	/θɪŋ/	/w/	want	/wɒnt/
/ɒ/	top	/tɒp/				/ð/	these	/ðiːz/	/j/	yes	/jes/

Audio scripts

UNIT 1

1.4 Lesson 1.3, Listening, Exercise B
H = Hamid S = Sarah

H: This coffee is good, isn't it?
S: Yes, it is! Hello, I'm Sarah.
H: Hi, Sarah. My name's Hamid Abboud.
S: Sorry? Ha …?
H: Hamid. H-A-M-I-D. Nice to meet you.
S: Nice to meet you, too, Hamid.
H: Are you a student here at the language school?
S: No, I'm not. I'm a teacher – an English teacher.
H: Oh! That's great! I'm a student on the design course. It's my first day.
S: Oh, great. Welcome. Where are you from, Hamid?
H: I'm from Egypt.
S: Oh, cool! Are you from Cairo?
H: No, I'm not. I'm from Alexandria.
S: Well, … um … See you soon. Oh! The design studio is in room number seven.
H: OK.
S: And the first class is at 10 o'clock.
H: Can you repeat that, please?
S: Yes, of course. It's at 10 o'clock.
H: Oh, OK. Thanks.
S: See you later!
H: Bye, Sarah.

1.5 Lesson 1.4, Functional Language, Exercise B
C = Callum L = Laura

C: Hi! My name's Callum. I'm from Canada.
L: Hello, Callum. Nice to meet you. I'm Laura. I'm from America.
C: Are you from New York?
L: No, I'm not. I'm from Boston.
C: Are you a student?
L: No, I'm a computer programmer. Are you a student?
C: Yes, I am.
L: Where are you from in Canada?
C: Vancouver.
L: What's your last name, Callum?
C: Westbrook. I'm Callum Westbrook. And you?
L: Price. Laura Price.
C: Well, um, nice to meet you, Laura. See you later.
L: Yes, see you in class.
C: OK, then. Bye.
L: Bye.

UNIT 2

2.3 Lesson 2.3, Listening, Exercise B
C = Carol R = Richard

C: Good morning. Music Box. Can I help you?
R: Oh, hello. Good morning. Is there music tonight?
C: No, sorry. Only tomorrow and Sunday.
R: Tomorrow?
C: Yes, tomorrow – Saturday.
R: What's on Saturday?
C: On Saturday at 11 am, there's a mariachi music workshop. It's with Pedro Rodriguez.
R: Who is Pedro Rodriguez?
C: He's a guitar teacher.
R: And what's mariachi music?
C: It's music from Mexico.
R: Hmm … I see. OK. What about Saturday evening?
C: Saturday evening? Um … it's African Music Night. Three different bands.
R: Where are they from?
C: From Mali, Morocco and Algeria.
R: Is it nice music?
C: Oh, yes. It's really fun.
R: What about Sunday?
C: On Sunday morning is … a singing workshop for children.
R: For children? Oh, no. No, thank you.
C: And on Sunday evening at eight … Istanbul Sound System.
R: What's the music?
C: It's jazz.
R: Hmm – no. The African Music Night. For three people.
C: OK. What's your name?
R: Richard Pitts.
C: Richard … Pitts. Saturday. 7 pm. That's fine. OK. See you on Saturday. Goodbye!
R: Thank you. Goodbye.

2.4 Lesson 2.4, Functional Language, Exercise B
Se = Sean M = Maria A = Aliki B = Ben So = Soraya

Se: Hi, everyone. Ben and Soraya are new students.
M: Hi! Please sit down and have some coffee.
A: Where are you from, Ben?
B: I'm from France. I'm French.
M: What's your job?
B: I'm a *créateur.*
M: A what? What does that mean?
Se: Designer. And what do you design?
B: I design clothes.
A: Oh. You're a fashion designer!
B: Yes, that's it.
Se: And what about you, Soraya?
So: I'm from Iran. I'm a … I think the English word is 'boss'.
M: A manager?
So: Yes, a manager.
E: I'm sorry, I don't understand. What do you manage?
So: It's my job. I'm the manager of a bank.

UNIT 3

3.4 Lesson 3.3, Listening, Exercise A
B = Bahati N = Naomi W = Waiter

B: Hello, Naomi. Sorry I'm late.
N: Hi, Bahati. That's OK. How's everything?
B: Good. And how are you?
N: I'm fine, thanks. Here – sit down.
W: Good afternoon. Coffee?
B: Yes, a cappuccino, please.
N: You have a lot of bags, Bahati!
B: Yes. I have some new things. A lot of new things! Look!
N: Red headphones? They're great!
B: Yes, yes, but look … a new phone!
N: Oh! It's super cool!
B: It's perfect!
N: What else?
B: A blue sweatshirt. And, glasses – for work.
N: The glasses are blue, too.
B: Yes, blue's my favorite color.
W: Here's your cappuccino.
B: Oh, thank you.

3.5 Lesson 3.4, Functional Language, Exercise B
A = Anna S = Sally

A: Hello, Anna here.
S: Hi, Anna. This is Sally.
A: I'm sorry? Sally?
S: Yes. Carl's sister.
A: Oh, yes! Hi, Sally. How are you?
S: I'm fine, thanks. Look, I have your hat. Do you want to meet? I can give it to you.
A: Yes. Thanks.
S: Um … Are you free at four o'clock?
A: Yes, I am.
S: Do you know Sam's Café?

A: Yes.
S: OK. See you there at four o'clock. Bye.
A: But, Sally!
S: Yes?
A: Do you have short hair … long hair …?
S: Oh, yes, of course! I have short light brown hair and … a red jacket.
A: OK. I have long black hair, a blue coat and a black scarf.

UNIT 4

4.4 Lesson 4.3, Listening, Exercise B
S = Simone K = Keith

S: Good morning and welcome to *Day by day*. Call and tell us all about your daily routine. What time do you get up, have breakfast, go to work …?
Hello! Good morning. What's your name?
K: I'm Keith Hatfield.
S: Hi, Keith. Tell us about your day. First of all, what's your job?
K: I work in a restaurant. It's called *Madeira to Madrid*.
S: Great! What kind of food is served in the restaurant?
K: We have Spanish and Portuguese food.
S: Hmm – yum! Is it a good job?
K: Yes, it is, but I go to work at five o'clock in the morning.
S: Oh, no!
K: Yes! I don't have breakfast at home. I have breakfast at work – at the restaurant.
S: Is it a big restaurant?
K: Yes, it is. And we have a lot of customers, so I'm always busy. I finish work at three o'clock in the afternoon. Then I go home and I take a nap for two hours!
S: And in the evening?
K: Um … In the evening, I talk to my friends on the phone, or we go out. We watch a movie or go to a café or restaurant to eat.
S: That's great! OK. Thanks, Keith! Bye!
K: Bye!

4.5 Lesson 4.4, Functional Language, Exercise B

A: Hello.
B: Good afternoon. What can I get you?
A: Can I have a cappuccino … no … some tea, please?
B: Of course. Small, medium or large?
A: Medium, please. To go.
B: And do you want milk with that?
A: Yes, please. Can I have a croissant, too?
B: Sorry, we don't have any croissants today.
A: Oh, OK. Just the tea, then.
B: Here you are.
A: Thanks. Bye!

UNIT 5

5.3 Lesson 5.3, Listening, Exercise A
W = Wendy S = Sam M = Mrs. Turner

W: Good morning, Mrs. Turner. Hi, Sam!
S: Hello.
M: Hi, Wendy. How are you?
W: I'm fine, thanks. So, Mrs. Turner, today is my first day with little Sam. Can you tell me about his day?

5.4 Lesson 5.3, Listening, Exercise B
W = Wendy S = Sam M = Mrs. Turner

M: Yes, of course. Um … Let me see. Sam has his breakfast at eight o'clock.
W: OK. What does he like to eat for breakfast?
M: He usually has bread and jam. And some milk, of course.
W: That's fine.
M: After breakfast, we usually go for a walk in the park, and Sam plays with his ball.
W: Where's his coat?
M: It's over there. It's blue.
W: It's cold today. Does he have a hat, too?
M: Yes, here it is. We usually eat lunch together. I don't cook a big meal at lunchtime. We have some eggs. Sam likes pasta, too.
W: Does Sam have juice to drink?
M: Oh, no. It has a lot of sugar. He drinks water.
W: OK. Does he take a nap in the afternoon?
M: Yes, for an hour.
W: I understand. And what time do you come home from work?
M: At four o'clock. But today is Thursday.
W: I don't understand.
M: Oh, sorry. I finish work early on Thursdays – at three o'clock.
W: Fine. See you at three o'clock.
M: Bye, Wendy. Bye, Sam.
S: Bye, Mommy!

5.5 Lesson 5.4, Functional Language, Exercise C
T = Ticket seller C = Customer

T: Can I help you?
C: I'd like a ticket to Rye, please.
T: That's $54 for a one-way ticket.
C: What time does it leave?
T: 11:30.
C: How long does it take?
T: About two hours.
C: How much is a round-trip ticket?
T: $102.
C: Wow! That's expensive. A one-way ticket to Rye, please.

UNIT 6

6.5 Lesson 6.3, Listening, Exercise A
A = Assistant W = William

A: Good morning. Can I help you?
W: Um … yes. I want to buy some new bedroom furniture. I'm a student here in the city. I have a new studio apartment. It's really nice, but there isn't any furniture.
A: I see. So you want …?
W: Um … first … I want a bed.
A: OK. This way, please. We have a lot of different styles and colors. Look.
W: Oh, yes. I like this one. It's blue and that's my favorite color.
A: Let me see … It's $270.
W: Oh, wow. That's very expensive.
A: How about this one? It's white. But it isn't very expensive – just $50.
W: Oh, yes. That's good. OK. And … I also want a desk.
A: Yes, of course. The desks are here. This brown desk is cheap. It costs $90.
W: Hmm – yes, it's a good price, but it's a bit small. How about that one?
A: Oh, yes. That's a nice desk, and it comes with a chair, too. The desk and the chair together cost $100.
W: Perfect. I'll take the desk with the chair.
A: Do you want a bookshelf?
W: Yes, I do, but I don't have any money for a bookshelf!
A: OK!
W: Can you bring the things to my new apartment?
A: Yes. No problem. What's your address?
W: It's Apartment 4b, 60 West Street.
A: OK. So … that's $150 altogether, please.
W: Here's my card.

A: Thank you.

W: Thanks very much. Goodbye.

A: Bye.

Lesson 6.4, Functional Language, Exercise C

W = Woman H = Helen J = Jimmy G = Gilbert R = Roberto

W: Excuse me. Is the museum near here?

H: The museum? Let me see. Oh … I'm not sure.

J: It's OK. I can tell you. It's not very far. Go out of the café. Turn right, then turn left. The museum is on your left.

G: No, that's the movie theater.

J: The movie theater's on the right, not the left.

G: No. The library is on the right. The movie theater is on the left.

H: OK, everybody. Let's just relax, OK?

R: Yes, calm down, everybody! Jimmy, Gilbert – you're both wrong. To get to the museum, you go out of the café, turn right, then left, then right, then left, then left again, and the museum's on your left.

W: Ah! Thank you.

1.1 Say hello

VOCABULARY

Countries

1 Canada **2** Brazil **3** Argentina **4** Mexico **5** Britain **6** Morocco **7** Japan **8** Italy **9** Egypt **10** Australia **11** Spain **12** Turkey

Numbers 0–10

A

b nine **c** three **d** six **e** two **f** ten **g** eight **h** four **i** seven **j** five

B

1 f **2** d **3** a **4** e **5** b **6** c

PRONUNCIATION

A

1 Spain **2** Japan **3** China/Egypt/Turkey **4** Egypt/Turkey/China **5** Turkey/China/Egypt **6** Italy/Mexico **7** Mexico/Italy **8** Morocco **9** Australia **10** Argentina

D

Ooo: Germany, Hungary
Oo: Russia, Sweden
oOoo: Colombia
ooOo: Indonesia

GRAMMAR

A

1 b **2** b **3** a **4** b **5** b **6** a

B

1 I am not from Spain / I'm not from Spain; No, I'm not
2 You are happy / You're happy; Are you happy
3 Am I from Egypt; Yes, I am

C

1 I'm **2** I'm **3** I'm **4** Are you **5** I'm not **6** I'm

1.2 What's your job?

VOCABULARY

A

q	c	o	m	p	u	t	e	r	p	r	o	g	r	a	m	m	e	r	r
d	o	c	t	o	r	t	y	s	o	c	c	e	r	p	l	a	y	e	r
e	n	g	i	n	e	e	r	o	s	h	k	l	p	m	s	b	r	p	e
x	n	t	p	m	m	q	k	o	c	a	s	u	v	u	s	p	a	d	c
t	m	b	u	i	l	d	e	r	h	r	t	c	b	s	f	h	m	l	e
e	f	v	a	n	r	q	r	g	e	d	u	a	t	i	z	o	a	p	p
a	s	d	r	n	r	z	r	h	f	y	d	w	s	c	v	t	n	y	t
c	j	d	e	s	i	g	n	e	r	d	e	r	u	i	u	o	a	q	i
h	o	y	c	t	o	g	s	c	b	e	n	r	o	a	i	g	g	u	o
e	p	t	c	p	h	p	k	z	a	m	t	e	a	n	l	r	e	r	n
r	a	r	w	r	i	t	e	r	a	u	j	a	c	k	l	a	r	d	i
h	c	q	f	i	t	l	k	r	l	s	c	p	c	t	r	p	h	b	s
l	t	n	s	a	l	e	s	c	l	e	r	k	a	n	t	h	k	n	t
p	o	l	i	c	e	o	f	f	i	c	e	r	c	e	a	e	v	n	m
a	r	c	h	i	t	e	c	t	r	r	o	c	t	w	w	r	u	v	e

B

1 a designer **2** manager **3** receptionist **4** a teacher
5 students **6** writer

GRAMMAR

A

1 is **2** isn't **3** It's **4** he's **5** it is **6** She's **7** Is it **8** not

B

1 he isn't **2** Is it **3** she is **4** He is / He's **5** It is / It's
6 Is she

PRONUNCIATION

B

1 b **2** a **3** b **4** a **5** b **6** a **7** b **8** a

1.3 Reading; Listening

READING

A

(in/at a language school) in New York City

B

1. She's a receptionist (at a language school).
2. It's big.
3. name, address, phone number
4. She's from Australia.
5. She's in the café.
6. Yes, he is.

C

2. a/the language school
3. my colleague / Anna
4. the café
5. my manager / David
6. your new job

LISTENING

B

They are in a café at the school.

C

1 Sarah **2** (English) teacher **3** Hamid **4** student
5 Egypt **6** 7 **7** 10 o'clock / 10 am

1.4 Functional Language; Fill in a form

FUNCTIONAL LANGUAGE

A

1 c **2** i **3** d **4** a **5** g **6** h **7** j **8** b **9** e **10** f

WRITING

A

Austria; Berlin; Helena; Jones; Simon; Stockholm
because they are all names of people and places

B

Alexander; **S**parks; **G**lasgow; **S**cotland

WRITING PRACTICE

Model answer

First name: Karen
Last name: Stewart
Home (city, country): Los Angeles, United States
Job: designer
Telephone number: 1 077 009 1453
Email: Karen.stewart@amail.net

2.1 Where are they from?

VOCABULARY

A

1 Brazilian **2** Chinese **3** Egyptian **4** Japanese **5** Malian
6 Polish **7** Swedish **8** Turkish

B

1 Algerian **2** Lebanese **3** Venezuelan **4** Italian
5 Vietnamese **6** Scottish **7** Portuguese **8** Danish

PRONUNCIATION

A

1. We're from Poland. We're Polish.
2. He's Canadian – you know, from Canada.
3. She's from Turkey. She's Turkish.
4. You're Swedish … from Sweden, right?
5. It's from Egypt. It's Egyptian.
6. The singer is from China. He's Chinese.
7. Alva is an Icelandic name. I'm from Iceland.
8. The songs are from Italy. They're in Italian.

GRAMMAR

Simple present *be*: *we, you, they*

1 Are you **2** We're **3** you **4** are **5** aren't **6** They're

Possessive adjectives

A

1 My **2** You **3** His **4** Its **5** She **6** Our **7** They

B

1 my **2** Its **3** Your **4** our **5** her **6** Their **7** His

2.2 When are you free?

VOCABULARY

Days of the week

A

1 Wednesday **2** Tuesday **3** Saturday **4** Monday
5 Thursday **6** Friday **7** Sunday

B

2 Tuesday **3** Wednesday **4** Thursday **5** Friday
6 Saturday **7** Sunday

Numbers 11–100

A

1 eleven **2** twenty **3** ninety **4** twelve **5** nineteen
6 thirty-six **7** fifty **8** fifteen

B

1 b 2 e 3 c 4 h 5 f 6 a 7 g 8 d

C

1 11 2 14 3 44 4 52 5 67 6 99

GRAMMAR

A

1 your name 2 are you 3 old are you 4 Who is / Who's
5 are their names 6 When are

B

1 Where **is** John ~~is~~ from? I don't think he is from the US.
2 I'm Ellen. What~~'s~~ is your name?
3 Jane's nice. Where ~~are~~ **is** she from?
4 Who~~'s~~ is your teacher? I have Mr. Smith.
5 How old **are** your children ~~are~~?
6 I love Anna Calvi. **Who** ~~What~~ is your favorite singer?
7 ~~From~~ **W**here is your English teacher **from**?
8 This class looks fun. How old **is** the teacher ~~is~~?

PRONUNCIATION

B

1 a 2 b 3 b 4 a 5 b 6 a

2.3 Reading; Listening

READING

A

Ireland

B

1 They're from Ireland, Canada, Britain and Australia.
2 Galway
3 Friday, Saturday and Sunday
4 Druve
5 Dublin
6 30/thirty

LISTENING

B

1 receptionist 2 Richard 3 African Music Night

C

1 11/eleven 2 Mexico 3 Mali 4 Sunday 5 Jazz

2.4 Functional Language; Write an online introduction

FUNCTIONAL LANGUAGE

Asking for clarification

A

1 new 2 from 3 job 4 What 5 mean 6 fashion
7 sorry 8 understand

WRITING

A

1 He's from Vienna.
2 He's 25 years old.
3 She's his (English) teacher.
4 She's from Des Moines / from Iowa.
5 Jazz

B

Hi, everybody! My name's Freddy and I'm from Vienna in Austria. I'm 25 years old and I'm an engineer. My English classes are on Mondays, Wednesdays and Fridays. My teacher is Mrs. Jane Cloud and she's from Edinburgh in Scotland. I'm a big fan of jazz. My favorite band is The Necks and they're from Australia.

WRITING PRACTICE

Model answer

Hi, everybody. My name's Erich and I'm from Berlin in Germany. I'm 19 years old and I'm a student. My English classes are on Tuesdays and Thursdays and my French classes are on Mondays, Wednesdays and Fridays. My English teacher is Mr. Peter James and he's from New York. I'm a big fan of African music and my favorite musicians are Salif Keita and Malombo.

3.1 That's my coat

VOCABULARY

A

s	m	b	r	o	s	l	u	e	t
w	y	e	l	l	o	w	e	d	b
b	l	u	w	n	g	r	e	e	r
l	l	o	w	a	c	k	e	r	o
a	c	k	r	e	d	g	o	e	w
c	g	r	e	u	o	r	e	y	n
k	p	i	n	t	r	a	b	b	c
w	h	i	l	t	e	y	s	k	v
w	g	r	e	e	n	t	x	a	h
h	c	l	l	o	d	s	a	l	m
i	b	r	o	u	d	e	t	c	h
t	r	e	a	d	g	h	t	a	n
e	d	s	a	y	b	l	u	e	i

B

1 hat 2 coat 3 bag 4 phone 5 glasses
6 headphones 7 sweatshirt 8 umbrella 9 glasses

GRAMMAR

a/an and plural nouns

1 a 2 b 3 b 4 b 5 b 6 b 7 a 8 a 9 a 10 b

this, that, these, those

1 This 2 Are these 3 those 4 This 5 that; this 6 These

PRONUNCIATION

B

1 /z/ 2 /s/ 3 /ɪz/ 4 /z/ 5 /s/ 6 /ɪz/

3.2 I have two sisters

VOCABULARY

A

1 son **2** wife **3** daughter **4** grandfather **5** grandparents
6 parents **7** husband **8** grandson

B

1 brother **2** husband **3** sisters **4** daughter
5 grandfather **6** children **7** parents **8** granddaughter's

C

1 wife's **2** sons **3** grandparents **4** father **5** mother
6 grandmother

PRONUNCIATION

A

1 mother **2** husband **3** umbrella **4** children
5 person **6** color

B

1 This is my broth<u>er</u>.
2 There's <u>a</u> party to cel<u>e</u>brate.
3 My fam<u>i</u>ly lives here.
4 Lilly isn't the oldest pers<u>o</u>n here.
5 Sally has two childr<u>e</u>n.
6 She doesn't have <u>a</u> husb<u>a</u>nd.

GRAMMAR

A

Conversation 1
1 Do **2** have **3** do **4** don't **5** have

Conversation 2
1 has **2** doesn't **3** Does **4** have **5** doesn't have **6** has

Conversation 3
1 have **2** do **3** have **4** don't have

B

2 I **don't have** ~~haven't not~~ a sister.
3 **B:** Yes, **I do** ~~I've do~~.
4 We **don't** ~~not~~ have an umbrella.
5 **Do** you have a big coat?
6 Marc **doesn't have** ~~haven't~~ a phone.
7 **We have** ~~We's~~ a class today.
8 Sam loves OneRepublic. He **has** ~~have~~ all their CDs.

3.3 Reading; Listening

READING

A

Suggested answer
something unusual/unexpected

B

A surprise birthday party for her at home with her family

C

1 F **2** F **3** T **4** T **5** F

LISTENING

A

1 In a café
2 Bahati

B

2, 3, 4, 7

C

1 e **2** c **3** a **4** d **5** b

3.4 Functional Language; Write a social media post

FUNCTIONAL LANGUAGE

A

1 long **2** dark **3** short **4** blond **5** glasses

B

1 sorry **2** hat **3** are **4** am **5** short **6** brown
7 jacket **8** blue

C

a Anna **b** Sally

WRITING

A

1 F **2** T **3** F **4** F

B

Two sentences which can be joined with *but*: I have a brother, too. He isn't here.
Rewritten as one sentence: I have a brother, too, but he isn't here.
Why do we use *but*?: To join ideas that are different.

WRITING PRACTICE

Model answer

Happy birthday to my colleague Deborah! Here we are at work – all the team! It's Deborah's 40th birthday today. She's the one with the cake and the big smile. She's very happy because it's her special day. That's our manager next to her with the glasses and the gray tie. His name's Paul. The other man with glasses and the striped tie is our colleague Dan. That's me with the curly hair. Birthdays are great, but now it's back to work.

4.1 Every day

VOCABULARY

Daily activities

1 get **2** have **3** go **4** finish **5** go **6** talk **7** go
8 read **9** watch **10** go

Time

A

1 g **2** h **3** b **4** d **5** f **6** e **7** c **8** a

B

a

b

c

d

e

f

g

h

i

j

GRAMMAR

A

2 live **3** go **4** don't go **5** finish **6** don't read
7 don't go **8** don't live

B

1 We relax in the evenings.
2 I don't live in a lighthouse.
3 You work in a school.
4 We don't play games on the computer.
5 I don't go out on Mondays.
6 They don't talk about work.
7 We finish work at six thirty.
8 They don't get up early on Sundays.

PRONUNCIATION

A

1 I get up at seven o'clock.
2 I have breakfast at home.
3 I go to work at eight in the morning.
4 I finish work at six thirty.
5 I don't go out in the evenings – I read or watch TV.
6 I go to bed at 11 o'clock.

B

1 They work in a hospital.
2 We have lunch together every Friday.
3 You don't start work until eight o'clock in the evening.
4 They teach English in Germany.
5 We get up at six o'clock in the morning.
6 The children don't watch TV in the morning.

4.2 Every year

VOCABULARY

A

1 March **2** October **3** June **4** May
5 September **6** January

B

1 March **2** winter **3** summer **4** June
5 spring **6** summer

C

1 summer **2** August **3** fall **4** October **5** winter
6 February **7** spring **8** April

GRAMMAR

A

1 b **2** c **3** a **4** c **5** b **6** c **7** a **8** b **9** c **10** c

B

1 do you
2 you work
3 do you get up
4 they go to bed
5 do you
6 you have

PRONUNCIATION

B

1, 3, 4, 6, 8

4.3 Reading; Listening

READING

A

cold

C

1 a **2** a **3** b **4** b **5** a

LISTENING

A

Picture b

B

1 on the radio **2** daily routines **3** has

C

1 Madrid **2** Portuguese **3** 5/five **4** breakfast
5 finish **6** nap

4.4 Functional Language; Write an email about your routine

FUNCTIONAL LANGUAGE

A

1 What can I get you
2 Can I have
3 Small
4 large
5 To go
6 do you want
7 please
8 Sorry

WRITING

A

1 (in the) afternoon
2 (at) one or two o'clock
3 (at) six o'clock (in the morning)
4 (in the) evening
5 (at) nine or ten o'clock
6 (at) seven o'clock

B

Hi Roberto,

How are you? I'm fine. I have a new job! I'm a postman now.

I get up at six o'clock in the morning, have breakfast and walk to work. I don't have a car. It's nice to work in the summer months. I finish work at one or two o'clock in the afternoon. It's not a long day. I go home and have lunch. And my wife, Gretel? She's at work in the afternoon, so I read a book or watch TV. In the evening, we have dinner at seven o'clock. I talk to my brother or my parents on the phone. We go to bed at nine or ten o'clock.

What about you? What's your routine?

Dev

P.S. Here's a photo of me doing my new job.

WRITING PRACTICE

Model answer

Hi Carlo,

How are you? I'm fine. It's Sunday, so I don't have any work. You ask what I do on my free days? Well, on Sundays, I get up late, at nine o'clock or nine thirty, and have coffee and make breakfast. I read the newspaper or watch the news on TV. Our son and daughter come for lunch at two o'clock and after lunch, we all go for a walk. In the evening, we play games and eat at home or go out to a restaurant. I go to bed at 9:30 because I get up for work at six o'clock on Monday.

What about you? What's your Sunday like?

Cecil

5.1 Relax and be happy

VOCABULARY

A

1 a **2** c **3** a **4** b **5** a **6** a

B

1 bath **2** walk **3** shopping **4** chess **5** meal
6 backyard **7** running **8** gym

C

1 When it's a nice day, we sit ~~at~~ **in** the backyard.
2 Do you want to go ~~for~~ running tomorrow?
3 Correct
4 Do they go **to** the gym every day?
5 In the afternoons, we play ~~at~~ chess.
6 On Saturdays, I go ~~for~~ shopping.
7 Correct
8 Why don't we go **for** a walk in the park?

GRAMMAR

A

1 b **2** c **3** a **4** c **5** a **6** a **7** b **8** a **9** b **10** c

B

1 Do your parents live **2** they do **3** cooks **4** doesn't cook
5 they don't **6** do they live **7** don't come **8** uses

PRONUNCIATION

A

1 he **2** she **3** he **4** she **5** she **6** he **7** she **8** he

5.2 When's your lunch break?

VOCABULARY

A

1 bread **2** juice **3** eggs **4** chicken **5** potatoes **6** fish
7 macaroni **8** rice **9** cheese **10** apple

B

Fruits: grapes; orange; pear
Vegetables: broccoli; cucumber; onion
Drinks: juice; milk; water
Snacks: chips; cookies; peanuts

GRAMMAR

A

1 I never eat chicken because I don't like it.
2 Most nights, I go to bed early. I'm frequently/usually in bed by 10 o'clock.
3 I sometimes eat fish because it's good for my health – but only once a month.
4 I'm always at the gym after work – I go every day of the week.
5 I sometimes run to work (about once a week), but I usually walk (about four times a week).

B

1 Jim ~~eats~~ frequently **eats** eggs.
2 We ~~eat~~ never **eat** late at night.
3 We ~~eat~~ sometimes **eat** lunch in a restaurant. / **Sometimes** we eat ~~sometimes~~ lunch in a restaurant.
4 We **are** always ~~are~~ busy on the weekends. / We'**re** always ~~are~~ busy on the weekends.
5 Ken ~~doesn't~~ never drink**s** milk.
6 I **am** always ~~am~~ late for work! / I'**m** always ~~am~~ late for work!
7 I ~~have~~ usually **have** a salad for lunch.
8 They don't ~~have~~ usually **have** breakfast.

PRONUNCIATION

A

1 She‿eats a lot of salad.
2 I‿often have eggs for breakfast.
3 The‿oranges are nice.
4 What does he‿eat for breakfast?
5 Tea‿is my favorite drink.
6 We‿often eat at home.
7 He‿always drinks coffee before work.

C

Tea or coffee? > I want to be an actor > Three eggs > She eats a lot of candy. > the end > Me and you

5.3 Reading; Listening

READING

A

1 The text talks about three countries.
2 The picture shows *huevos rancheros*, a Mexican breakfast.

B

1 F 2 F 3 T 4 T 5 F 6 F

LISTENING

A

1 Wendy
2 Mrs. Turner

B

1 b 2 b 3 a

C

1 bread and jam
2 plays
3 blue
4 hat
5 pasta
6 doesn't have
7 one hour / an hour / 1 hour
8 four o'clock / 4:00 / 4 / 4 o'clock

5.4 Functional Language; Write a blog post about food

FUNCTIONAL LANGUAGE

A

1 How long does it take?
2 How much is a round-trip ticket?
3 I'd like a ticket to Rye, please.
4 What time does it leave?

B

1 I'd like a ticket to Rye, please.
2 What time does it leave?
3 How long does it take?
4 How much is a round-trip ticket?

WRITING

A

1 an office 2 usually 3 Her colleagues eat 4 sometimes

B

1 it 2 her 3 They 4 we 5 them

WRITING PRACTICE

B

Model answer

I regularly come home on the weekends because I love it when all the family is together and we have a big meal. Sometimes I cook, but usually my mother cooks our Sunday lunch. Today, there is chicken with potatoes and some vegetables. We all help – my father and my brother and two sisters – and I usually bring something. Today, it's a cake and ice cream for dessert. Sunday lunch with my family is my favorite meal.

6.1 Around town

VOCABULARY

A

			1h								
			o								
			t		2p						3m
	4m		e		a						u
5g	a	l	l	e	r	y					s
	r				k		6s	t	o	r	e
	k			7c			t				u
8r	e	s	t	a	u	r	a	n	9t		m
	t			f			t		h		
				é			i		e		
							o		a		
							n		t		
									e		
									r		

B

1 station 2 park 3 café 4 gallery 5 restaurant
6 theater 7 market 8 stores

GRAMMAR

A

1 a 2 a 3 b 4 b 5 b 6 a 7 b 8 a 9 b 10 a
11 a 12 b

B

1 f 2 d 3 b 4 e 5 a 6 c

6.2 Choosing a home

VOCABULARY

Furniture and rooms

a kitchen b bathroom c living room

1 oven 2 fridge 3 shower 4 mirror 5 toilet 6 rug
7 coffee table 8 couch

Prepositions of place

1 in 2 under 3 on 4 on 5 in

GRAMMAR

A

1 Is there
2 Are there
3 Is there
4 Is there
5 Are there
6 Is there

B

1 Is there 2 there is 3 Are there 4 there aren't
5 Is there 6 there are 7 Are there 8 there aren't
9 Is there 10 there is 11 Are there 12 there aren't

PRONUNCIATION

B

1 a 2 b 3 a 4 b 5 a

C

1 /ʌ/ 2 /ʌ/ 3 /e/ 4 /ʌ/ 5 /e/ 6 /ʌ/ 7 /e/ 8 /ʌ/

D

1 bread 2 run 3 bus 4 bed 5 them 6 mom
7 tent 8 let

6.3 Reading; Listening

READING

A

Both cities have beautiful old buildings. The buildings in Edinburgh look like the buildings of ancient Athens.

B

a 4 b 2 c 1 d 3

C

1 Scotland
2 learn about history
3 busy
4 not far
5 enjoys
6 a good view

LISTENING

A

1 There isn't
2 hasn't
3 a bed, a desk and a chair

B

a 3 b 5 c 2 d 1 e 4

C

1 apartment
2 white
3 100 / one hundred
4 bookshelf
5 60

6.4 Functional Language; Write a review of a café

FUNCTIONAL LANGUAGE

A

art gallery

B

1 Turn
2 turn
3 on
4 movie theater
5 library
6 left

WRITING

A

The writer likes the café because the staff is friendly, the croissants, music and coffee are all good, there is free wi-fi and it isn't always busy.

B

1 T 2 F 3 F 4 T

C

1 b 2 d 3 a 4 e 5 c

WRITING PRACTICE

B

Model answer

A good café is quiet with good, cheap food and drink and free wi-fi. Amy's Café isn't like that. I don't like it because there are always a lot of people talking and you can't hear because of the music. The chairs aren't comfortable and the color of the walls is horrible! The hot chocolate and the coffee are OK, but they're very expensive. You sometimes wait an hour for a snack or some soup because it's always very busy. There's free wi-fi, but it never works, so you can't check your emails and messages.

Notes

Notes

Notes